S0-AXV-042

JUMBO CROSSWORD PUZZLES

Volume 2

BENDON®
Publishing International, Inc.
© 2009
Ashland, OH 44805
www.bendonpub.com

PUZZLE 1

ACROSS

1 Booted
5 Rent
10 Obligation
14 Jacob's son
15 Indian weapon
16 Decorative needle case
17 Greek god of war
18 Heading
19 Respiratory organ
20 Pachisi, alt. spelling
22 Breadth
23 Band instrument
24 Morse code dash
26 Time zone
27 Water
30 Fox holes
33 Swine
35 Among
37 Religious skepticism
42 Not yours
43 TV lawyer Matlock
44 Healing plant

45 Examples
49 Not minus
50 Wing
51 Beep
53 Resort hotel
54 Thai
57 Abdominal muscles (abbr.)
59 Evergreen tree
61 Old
63 Nomad home producer
69 Wrack
70 Eagle's nest
71 Brand of milk
72 Lump
73 Baby sheep
74 Pitcher
75 Head coverings
76 Bomb
77 Dreadful

DOWN

1 Cuff
2 Juno
3 Concluded
4 Records
5 Stretchy materials
6 Canal
7 Branch of learning
8 Not gas or liquid
9 Ram's mate
10 Cafe
11 Musical composition
12 Taps the baseball lightly
13 Waterproofed
21 Held
22 Hold it there
25 Sign language
27 Wet
28 Ruler
29 Alcoholic drink
31 Northeast by east
32 Aroma
34 Cover a present
36 Prefix ten

38 To
39 Evils
40 Bisque
41 Plateau
46 Dash
47 Swab
48 Least hard
52 Dickens' Tiny __
54 Olympic fire holder
55 Birds "thumb"
56 Dope
58 Creep away
60 Ranted
62 Ceases
64 Writer Bombeck
65 Small licorice treats
66 Chinese gooseberry
67 Always
68 Exotic
70 Loose gown worn at mass

PUZZLE 2

ACROSS

1 Fish
5 Dice game
10 Sweet potatoes
14 Bottom
15 Stays out of sight
16 Assure
17 Brand of sandwich cookie
18 Found
19 Item for sale
20 Polygon surrounded solid
22 Book by Homer
23 Drunkard
24 Not (refix)
26 Caustic substance
27 Hertz
30 Wide open
33 Avail
35 Den
37 Crustacean (2wds.)
42 Capital of Norway
43 Body of water
44 What a bald man is missing
45 Visited three bears (2 wds.)
49 Vegetable
50 Vane direction
51 Adolescent
53 Time zone
54 Hoopla
57 W.C.
59 River (Spanish)
61 Variety show
63 Twinge (2 wds.)
69 Concluded
70 Sporty car brand
71 Small pipe
72 Hum
73 Car parker
74 Bulb flower
75 Otherwise
76 Efface
77 Mold

DOWN

1 Cube
2 Air (prefix)
3 Rotate
4 Clever plans
5 Fast feline
6 Layer
7 Jewish calendar month
8 Pie nut
9 Fast plane
10 Ship's small boat
11 To no __
12 Eel
13 Swedish citizen
21 Shoat
22 Institution (abbr.)
25 French "yes"
27 Jam
28 El __
29 Window ledge
31 Mexican money
32 Construct
34 Reverberate
36 Traveled by car
38 Earn
39 Skim
40 Ventilates
41 Rascal
46 Island
47 Sign of the zodiac
48 Jagged
52 Snip
54 Got up
55 Lucifer
56 Bakers needs
58 Sesame Street's grouch
60 Ocular
62 Goad
64 __ hoop
65 Greek god of war
66 Nimbus
67 Wading bird
68 Bird's home
70 Street abbr.

PUZZLE 3

ACROSS

1 Parts of plays
5 Insects
10 Southwest by south
14 Leaky faucet noise
15 Once more
16 Excuse me!
17 Information
18 Moses' mountain
19 Dorothy's dog
20 What an angry animal does
22 Land workers
24 Drag
25 Make a record of
27 Ablaze
29 Special case only (2 wds.)
32 Medication amounts
35 Muffin ingredient
38 Time period
39 Caution
40 Place
41 Muscle builder
43 Tell a tall tale
44 Dieter's joy
46 Absent
47 Was
48 Strong metal
49 Smooth tightly twisted thread
51 Hit
54 Leaven
57 Make lace
59 Norwegian
62 Eyed
64 Wading bird
66 Leading
68 Run easily
69 Dregs
70 Type of Greek column
71 Fencing sword
72 Otherwise
73 Greek island
74 Appear

DOWN

1 Totals
2 Type of water bird
3 Huge
4 Ancient Greek citizen
5 Old-fashioned Fathers
6 Aegis
7 Sound
8 Jeweled headdress
9 Smell
10 Rested
11 Less than retail
12 Second letter of the greek alphabet
13 Haze
21 Headed
23 Two __ (has two faces)
26 Gone With the Wind's Mr. Butler
28 Propel with oars
30 Unrefined metal
31 Christmas __
33 Canal
34 Was looked at
35 Prohibits
36 Revel
37 Pardons
39 Wee
41 Beauty __
42 French "yes"
45 Female (abbr.)
47 Hound dogs
50 Sign of the zodiac
52 Theme
53 Inaccuracy
55 Tilt
56 Wigwam
57 Floor covering
58 Cain killed him
60 Cosecant's opposite
61 Shine
63 View as
65 South southeast
67 Whiz

ANSWER KEY

PUZZLE 73

PUZZLE 76

PUZZLE 74

PUZZLE 77

PUZZLE 75

PUZZLE 78

ANSWER KEY

PUZZLE 79

PUZZLE 81

PUZZLE 80

PUZZLE 4

ACROSS

1 Shorten (abbr.)
5 Tippet
10 Northwest by west
14 Sheaf
15 Island
16 Prophet who built the arc
17 Epochs
18 Seize
19 Canal
20 Slow
22 Leaves
24 Eye infection
25 Scrub clean
27 Dryad
29 Bread leftover
32 Stand up
35 Office furniture
38 Sign of the zodiac
39 Crustacean
40 Southwestern Indian
41 Actor Branagh
43 The __ (final word)
44 Word processor blinker
46 United States of America
47 Jittery
48 Jeweled headdress
49 What a dropped melon does
51 Covers with gold
54 Output
57 Sign language
59 Pointed at
62 Slouch
64 Capital of Western Samoa
66 Gas
68 Taboo
69 Crucifix
70 Pain reliever brand
71 After awhile
72 Post-Traumatic Stress Disorder
73 Catch some Zs
74 Harp

DOWN

1 Cain killed him
2 Uncovers
3 Mont __
4 Done to market shelf items
5 Compass point
6 Feel concern
7 Charge card
8 Bow's need
9 Greasy
10 North northeast
11 Loved
12 Tempt
13 Curds and __
21 Possessive pronoun
23 Break
26 Monarch
28 For
30 Women's partners
31 Incentive
33 Ditty
34 Whirl
35 Conduit
36 Decorative needle case
37 Large harems
39 European country
41 Australian bear
42 Sixth sense
45 __ Lanka
47 Forever
50 Relief
52 Female lead singers
53 Puny
55 Nutty
56 Giver
57 Retired persons association (abbr.)
58 Descry
60 Fencing sword
61 Noah's bird
63 Cornmeal cake
65 Adorn
67 Representative

PUZZLE 5

ACROSS

1. What babies do
6. Eve's husband
10. Vassal
14. Files
15. Bare
16. Spoken
17. Eyed
18. Prayer ending
19. Sole
20. Gofer
21. Caesar's three
22. Mainland State
24. Northwest by north
26. Spooks
27. Lustrous
30. Tinted
31. Wet
32. Coarse
33. Computer part
36. Fat
37. Status ___
38. Italian "dollars"
40. Goof
41. Cut of beef
43. Stupid
44. Food
45. Veered
46. Think
49. Eye
50. Studies
51. Crow's call
52. Stink
56. Cab
57. Serving dish
59. Devil
60. Usages
61. Soothe
62. Accustom
63. Fox holes
64. Tinter
65. Steps for crossing a fence

DOWN

1. Let fall
2. Be in a ___
3. Capital of Norway
4. Frankness
5. Acid
6. Vigorously
7. Less than usual in size, power or character
8. Is
9. Endangered
10. Relating to the sun
11. Jagged
12. Positions
13. Tiny insect
21. Large computer company
23. Polite
25. Boatman
26. Governing group
27. Famous cookies
28. Mongolian desert
29. Legal claim
30. Scare
32. Small group
33. Animal stomach
34. Window ___
35. Old
39. Infallible
42. Electromagnetism discoverer
45. Tailor
46. Utilize
47. Dine
48. Total
49. Cover
50. Glorify
51. Court suit
53. Decorative needle case
54. Duke
55. Joint
58. Visible light
59. Sister for short

PUZZLE 6

ACROSS

1 Legion
6 Valley
10 Baseball team
14 English sailor
15 Pixies
16 Canal
17 Ablaze
18 Male children
19 Ocean Spray's drink starters
20 Peter, for short
21 Butane
22 Accompany
24 Reasons
26 Capital of Turkey
27 In bloom
30 Agency (abbr.)
31 Hand grips
32 Coaxed
33 Miles per hour
36 Toward the rear of the ship
37 Bard's before
38 American state
40 Saloon
41 Fish tank growth
43 Watch
44 End
45 Spookily
46 Countermand
49 Feel concern
50 Most confident
51 Creative work
52 Shellfish
56 Spoken
57 Promotion
59 Flint
60 Speedy
61 Soothe
62 Narrow openings
63 Brews
64 Rushed
65 Kinds

DOWN

1 Applaud
2 Abundant
3 Elide
4 Silver bullet target
5 Change color
6 Permissions to enter foreign countries
7 Famous cookies
8 Licensed practical nurse
9 Marrow
10 Holy city
11 Inaccuracy
12 Jeweled headdress
13 Delivered by post
21 Exercise place
23 Parachute user
25 Held for ransom (plural)
26 Harmonize
27 Middle East dweller
28 Baby's "ball"
29 Prevaricator
30 Relating to the hearing
32 Lawful
33 Wise Man
34 Mr. Donahue
35 Sacred
39 Instantly
42 Abhors
45 Munch
46 Agrarian
47 Efface
48 Rains hard
49 Teachings
50 Lounge
51 Recess
53 Knit
54 Wager
55 Dining hall
58 Talk
59 Fast plane

PUZZLE 7

ACROSS

1 Gets older
5 Swiftly
10 Rope fiber
14 Groove
15 Plazas
16 Aroma
17 Air (prefix)
18 Jell-o salad
19 Flat bread
20 Woven on a board
22 Small
23 Label
24 Adios
26 Distress call
27 Been
30 Shina
33 Imp
35 Seaweed substance
37 Crazed
42 Heal
43 Accountant
44 Capital of Norway
45 Create wind catchers
49 Disfigure
50 Talk
51 Tinted
53 Bog
54 Klutz
57 Average work performance
59 Place
61 Former wounds
63 Without instrumental accompaniment
69 Opera solo
70 Philippine dish with marinated chicken or pork
71 Pliers
72 Lotion brand
73 Lining
74 Rate
75 Association (abbr.)
76 Gourmet chocolate brand
77 Jittery

DOWN

1 Middle East dweller
2 Movie __
3 European monetary unit
4 Ermine
5 Mixture
6 El __
7 Dog food brand
8 Hike a mountain
9 Escudo
10 N.A. Indian
11 Blue-pencil's
12 Slogan
13 Begs
21 Parent
22 Sash
25 Aye
27 Western Athletic Conferences
28 Water (Sp.)
29 Japanese dress
31 Lava
32 Drugged
34 "To:'s" partner
36 Depend
38 Not one
39 U.S. Air Force
40 Indication
41 German city
46 Charts
47 Precedes an alias
48 Harbor
52 Vegetable dunk
54 City
55 Land
56 Carnivals
58 Radiuses
60 M
62 Pour
64 Connecticut (abbr.)
65 Upon restful furniture
66 Cargo
67 Want
68 Alcoholic
70 Entire

PUZZLE 8

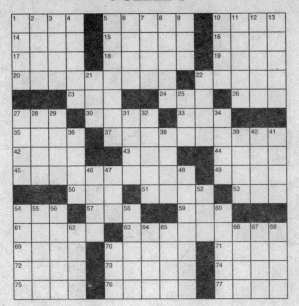

ACROSS

1 Gets older
5 Steals
10 Light
14 Candy bar Baby __
15 Unmerited
16 American state
17 Horse hair
18 Stone
19 Oceans
20 Signet (2 wds.)
22 Supports
23 Contender
24 __ Lanka
26 Perish
27 Body of water
30 Trudge
33 Curve
35 __-a-sketch
37 Washing machine locale
42 Cab
43 Carve
44 Weight unit
45 Idea symbols
49 Spy
50 French "yes"
51 Irritation
53 Distress call
54 Vane direction
57 I want my ___
59 Limb
61 Drinks quickly
63 Airplane tail assembly
69 Tiny insect
70 Sing softly
71 Region
72 Not ins
73 Association (abbr.)
74 Beats
75 Rushed
76 Woodworker's tool
77 Satiate

DOWN

1 Weapons
2 Small island
3 Bunsen burner
4 Book holder
5 Actor Crowe
6 Wager
7 Notion
8 Takes the edge off
9 Visit
10 Fail to keep
11 In the lead
12 Florida City
13 Police
21 Snip
22 Energy
25 Really cool
27 Make tight
28 Decorative needle case
29 Acting (abbr.)
31 Next to Kauai
32 Fights
34 Pepsi rival
36 Santa call (2wds.)
38 Northwest by north
39 Drop leave out
40 Dog food brand
41 Children's love
46 "Calciums" antacid brand
47 Whit
48 Muffle
52 X
54 Kellogg's waffles
55 Day's beginning
56 Thrill
58 Vice __
60 Chew like a rodent
62 Post-traumatic stress disorder
64 Greatest amount
65 Winnie the __
66 Opera solo
67 Male
68 Soothe
70 Calorie

PUZZLE 9

ACROSS

1. Compose
4. Root beer brand (3 wds.)
9. Like cloth
14. Brew
15. Bride's dishes
16. Demean
17. Badger
18. Become less tight
19. Grant an extension
20. Jeweled headdress
22. Unpredictable
24. Opposed
25. Arm extension
27. Celebrity
31. Was looked at
32. Dance
33. Ram's mate
34. Wanderer
36. Seasoned rice
38. Order
40. Honorably
42. African nation
43. Mongrels
44. Wrestling mat
45. Cut of beef
47. Otherwise
51. Outer layer
53. National capital
54. Garish
55. Black gem
57. Hunting expedition
59. Outwit
62. Listlessness
65. Valentine mo.
66. From Asia
67. Garbed
68. Wing
69. Brand of Tile game
70. Swedish citizen
71. Change color

DOWN

1. Black and white animals
2. Character on "Seinfeld"
3. Belie
4. Land unit
5. Excuse me!
6. Goose egg
7. Genetic code
8. Growing
9. Jetty
10. Complies
11. Wheeled vehicle
12. Vane direction
13. Latest
21. Light rowboat
23. Food and drug administration (abbr.)
25. Legion
26. One of these
28. Signal
29. Out
30. Umpire
32. Hertz
35. Yes
36. Pacific Standard Time
37. Its own
38. Boyfriend
39. Ceases
40. Month
41. Southwestern Indian
42. Rate
43. Mama
45. Chance
46. Fighters
48. Bummed
49. Certainly
50. Nonpoisonous
52. Film maker
56. Taboo
57. Took to court
58. Military officer
59. Paddle
60. United States of America
61. Facial twitch
63. This time
64. North by east

PUZZLE 10

ACROSS

1 I want my ___
4 Transparent gem
9 Trades
14 Caesar's three
15 Adios
16 Make a letter
17 American Cancer Society (abbr.)
18 Type of car
19 Soap
20 Plant organ
22 Surgical garment
24 Wise Man
25 Looked
27 Tennis player Steffi
31 Pros
32 Fat
33 Wing
34 Homeless people
36 Sesame Street's grouch
38 Brand of pain reliever
40 Molds
42 Explode
43 Island nation
44 Highest trump in some loo
45 Jump
47 Exotic
51 Father
53 Green Gables dweller
54 At sea
55 Season
57 Compelling to go
59 One-celled animal
62 Muslim's religion
65 New Jersey's neighbor
66 Disease cause
67 Khaki cotton twill
68 Ram's mate
69 Opposite of ally
70 Looks for
71 Fast plane

DOWN

1 Noxious vapor
2 Breath mint
3 Face
4 Elemental
5 Adam's garden
6 Free of
7 Yes
8 Surges
9 Compass point
10 Amiss
11 Sky
12 School group
13 Gender
21 Accident
23 Poem
25 Black
26 Aye
28 Speed
29 Alack's partner
30 Distant
32 Kimono sash
35 Fall mo.
36 Cereal
37 Helix
38 Middle East dweller
39 Desensitize
40 Sold at a discount
41 Smash
42 Environmental protection agency (abbr)
43 Attila the ___
45 Wheeled vehicle
46 Pranks
48 Side notes
49 Grants an extension
50 Baby eagle
52 Record
56 Uncomplicated
57 Ball player ___ Aaron
58 Famous cookies
59 Street abbr.
60 Least amount
61 Bard's before
63 Her
64 Tell a tall tale

PUZZLE 11

ACROSS

1 On top
5 Thunder
9 Eyed
14 Italian currency
15 Writer Bombeck
16 Where you were at crime time
17 Cain killed him
18 Nab
19 Burial sites
20 River (Spanish)
21 Gaelic
23 Pear type
24 Geology
26 Poem
28 Thai
29 Black
31 Second day of the week.
34 Carrot nutrient
37 Store
39 Prego's competition
40 Street abbr.
41 Recess
42 1997 Madonna movie
44 Downey role
47 Bog
48 Curds and __
50 Still
51 Thirst quencher
52 Shopping malls
56 Soybean
59 Back talks
63 American Kennel Club (abbr.)
64 Questions
66 Professional football team
67 Cook pottery
68 Computer characters
69 Malaria
70 Flatten
71 Begin
72 Sheet of matted cotton
73 DNA component

DOWN

1 Fright
2 Shinbone
3 Sandwich cookies brand
4 Crony
5 Behalf
6 Spoken
7 Elide
8 French Sudan
9 Cereal
10 World map
11 Fancy car
12 Tides
13 Saucer
21 Hello!
22 Cry softly
25 Swagger
27 Genetic code
29 Legate
30 Veal
31 Sticky fastener
32 Soviet Union
33 Vane direction
34 Grotto
35 Against
36 Soothe
38 Ray
39 Umpire
43 Respect
45 Compose
46 Snaky fish
49 In possession of
51 S.E. Asian mammal
53 Belgian Congo
54 City in Ohio
55 Setting
56 Baths
57 Throw out
58 Young Men's Christian Association
60 Middle East dweller
61 Heroic tale
62 Indecent language
65 Be seated
67 Fruit

PUZZLE 12

ACROSS

1 Dull
5 Mom
9 Lady
14 Nimbus
15 Gets older
16 "Remember the ___"
17 Cadge
18 Before ten
19 Bird claw
20 McDonald's "Big ___"
21 Yearly
23 Hazard
24 Strong chemical base
26 Eye infection
28 ___ Francisco
29 Togs
31 Constrictor snake
34 Can chips
37 Tall post
39 Tropical bird
40 Unrefined metal
41 Slimly
42 Lick
44 Positive
47 Convert into leather
48 Unpredictable
50 Rodent
51 Thai
52 Plant lice
56 Island nation
59 Bombs
63 Received
64 Belonging to Eve's husband
66 Reverberate
67 ___ matter
68 Gallops
69 Make a whizzing sound
70 Author
71 Notify
72 Renounce
73 Flip

DOWN

1 Lava
2 Relating to the hearing
3 Van
4 Charge
5 Piloting
6 Against
7 List of meals
8 At sea
9 Tangle
10 Wing shaped
11 Painter of melting clocks
12 Famous cookies
13 Nun's counterpart
21 Actor Alda
22 Acid
25 From Asia
27 Teaspoon (abbr.)
29 Horse race
30 Usages
31 Absorb
32 Slime
33 One of these
34 Dad
35 Baseball's Nolan
36 Linger
38 Young person
39 Mountain Standard Time
43 Killed in action
45 Small chapel
46 What dogs sit on
49 False story
51 Kitchen timepiece
53 Eskimo home
54 Vaulted ceilings
55 Statistics
56 Syllables used in songs (2 wds.)
57 Movie star
58 Jest
60 Ribald
61 Pound
62 Shinny
65 Fast plane
67 Inclined

PUZZLE 13

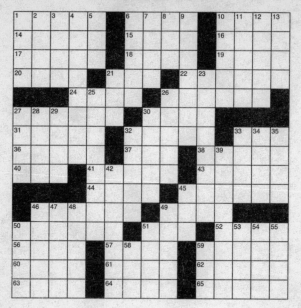

ACROSS

1 Workers
6 Baby's "ball"
10 Adoring
14 Globe
15 Prayer ending
16 Brand of sandwich cookie
17 Protective covering
18 Delivered by post
19 Reside
20 Tryout
21 Nothing
22 Abominable
24 Movie star
26 Purple vegetables
27 Famous Russian Ruler
30 Removes the water
31 Shells
32 Thousands of sheets of paper
33 Animal foot
36 Right angle to a ship's length
37 Entire
38 Era
40 Been
41 Speak without preparation
43 Undemanding
44 Mouth parts
45 Scratches
46 Dough
49 Hazard
50 Baseball's Strawberry
51 Thai
52 Writer Bombeck
56 Academy (abbr.)
57 Computer picture button
59 Cured
60 Spouse
61 Spruce
62 Rumormonger
63 Pitcher
64 Heavenly beings
65 Lawn tool

DOWN

1 Hit
2 Ripped up
3 Weapons
4 Fleet of ships
5 Popular president's initials
6 Herb
7 Charge card
8 TV lawyer Matlock
9 Opposite meaning
10 Folded sheet of paper
11 Constellation
12 Birthmark
13 Bucks wives
21 Not (refix)
23 Cuts up
25 Cheerlessly
26 Toothbrush brand
27 George Bernard ___
28 Brass
29 Brews
30 Cafes
32 Movie "King"
33 Swanky
34 Pound
35 Reasons
39 Pursed
42 Calling on phone
45 Caesar's three
46 Popinjay
47 Speak
48 Arrangement
49 ___ and raves
50 Lady
51 Frog's cousin
53 Chime
54 Dole out
55 Jewish calendar month
58 Corporate top dog
59 Change color

PUZZLE 14

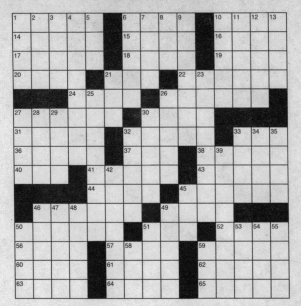

ACROSS

1 Avoids
6 Japanese dress
10 Totals
14 Listlessness
15 Tribe
16 Bisque
17 Relaxes
18 Charity
19 Ancient Indian
20 Soft cheese from Greece
21 Travel
22 What you say after "please"
24 What a clock tells
26 Laughing dogs
27 Staring
30 Quieted
31 Not dead
32 How you got along
33 Fast plane
36 Type of communication
37 Choose
38 Hippopotamus' nickname
40 __ you! (attention getter)
41 Fashion capital
43 Dope
44 Dash
45 Representatives
46 Badly
49 Reverberate
50 Dwarf's opposites
51 Hatchet
52 Weight unit
56 Meshes
57 Roman garments
59 Outline
60 Pound
61 Truant
62 Unit of electric power
63 Compass point
64 Engage
65 Alpha's opposite

DOWN

1 Vassal
2 Joint
3 Institution (abbr.)
4 Reputed
5 Sister for short
6 Balancer
7 Unite
8 Ewe's mate
9 Vogue (2 wds.)
10 From Asia
11 Title of Italian woman
12 Shirks
13 Baths
21 Madagascar franc (abbr.)
23 Aloft (2 wds.)
25 Amateurish
26 Aches
27 Swearword
28 Gaiety
29 Spring flower
30 Rabbit
32 Inroad
33 Revolve
34 Descry
35 Children
39 Symbolic representer
42 Entirely outstanding performers (2 Wds.)
45 Whiz
46 Bit
47 Promises
48 Beginning
49 Glorify
50 Chew
51 Competition at the Greek games
53 Tempo
54 Acting (abbr.)
55 Plateau
58 IOU part
59 Couple

PUZZLE 15

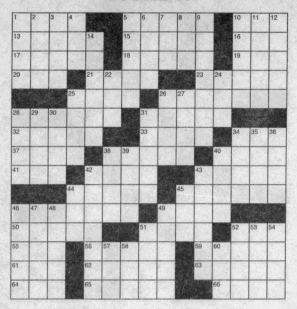

ACROSS

1 Beehive State
5 Association (abbr.)
10 Drag
13 Beverage
15 Avow
16 Abridged (abbr.)
17 Layered
18 Desert plants
19 Note of debt
20 Brew
21 Move through the water
23 Plant
25 N.A. Indian
26 Stalkers
28 Distort
31 Emblem
32 Toothbrush brand
33 Aroma
34 South southeast
37 Floor covering
38 Brisk
40 Opp. of early
41 Body of water
42 Singer Billy
43 Type of mushroom
44 Fork prongs
45 Spring flower
46 Abided by
49 Pope John ___
50 Twisted
51 Formal
52 Fast plane
55 Neither's partner
56 Infuse
59 Undo the laces
61 Stretch to make do
62 Dapper
63 Connect
64 Crimson
65 Stuffs
66 Small bird

DOWN

1 Ca. University
2 Work hard
3 Teen disease
4 Garden tool
5 Computer characters
6 Played in the water
7 Part of a min.
8 Cereal
9 Fridge fruit storer
10 Thieves' hideouts
11 Around
12 Bear food
14 Suck up
22 Typing rate
24 That man
25 Sock's wound
26 Bars
27 On top
28 Points
29 Canal
30 Syllables used in songs (2 wds.)
31 Grinds
34 Japanese dress
35 Stair
36 Snaky fish
38 Pine tree product
39 Woodwind instrument's need
40 Lounge
42 Dancing Irish style
43 Frock
44 Can metal
45 Thai
46 Proprietor
47 Bust
48 Coaxed
49 Hunts
51 Golf swing
52 Move while sleeping
53 Location
54 Adolescent
57 Bad (prefix)
58 Heat unit
60 North northwest

PUZZLE 16

ACROSS

1 Opaque gem
5 Muslim's religion
10 Farm credit administration (abbr.)
13 City
15 Trusting
16 Serving of corn
17 What a helicopter needs
18 BB Player Abdul Jabar
19 Microgram
20 Vane direction
21 Use a keyboard
23 Mickey's dog
25 Eat sparingly
26 Receive by bequest
28 Stone
31 Tress
32 Metal bolt
33 Ventilates
34 Estimated time of arrival
37 Won
38 Donald's girlfriend
40 Alliance
41 TV lawyer Matlock
42 False bible god
43 Wind
44 Happy cat sounds
45 Planet
46 Awkward step
49 "Ribbit" animal
50 To that time
51 Pain
52 Container
55 Sign of the zodiac
56 Heron
59 Use
61 European sea eagle
62 Hoist
63 Dine
64 Eye infection
65 Narrow openings
66 Give

DOWN

1 Giant
2 Gofer
3 Wager
4 W.C.
5 Awkward
6 One's good
7 Tell a tall tale
8 Street abbr.
9 Graceland
10 Bone
11 Desert plants
12 Jargon
14 Creator
22 Aye
24 Headed
25 Expired
26 Bulb flower
27 Not one
28 Take away
29 Pleasant
30 Flat
31 Scoops out water
34 Dash
35 Meat alternative
36 Parts of plays
38 Challenge
39 Retired persons association (abbr.)
40 Boast
42 Menservants
43 Windsock
44 Pounds per square inch
45 Pot
46 Beasts of burden
47 Inanimate
48 Hardhearted
49 Destinies
51 Annoyance
52 Moderate
53 Elderly
54 DNA component
57 Young lady
58 River (Spanish)
60 Pouch

PUZZLE 17

ACROSS

1 Lashed boat
5 Young pigeon
10 Famous ski resort
14 Women's magazine
15 Liquid measurement
16 Ancient Indian
17 Ordain
18 Dry stream bed
19 After awhile
20 Stews
22 Warble
24 Less than two
25 Ego discoverer
27 Ermine
29 Quake
32 Whop
35 Spruce
38 Time period
39 Typewriter roller
40 Adorn
41 Rigidly
43 Poem
44 Rates
46 Note of debt
47 Sailors
48 White vegetable
49 Protective covering
51 Respond
54 Customer
57 Farm credit administration (abbr.)
59 Used the oars in a boat
62 Tiny island
64 Lubricates
66 Simulate
68 Technical
69 Fence opening
70 Equipped
71 Malaria
72 Soybean
73 Petty fights
74 Harp

DOWN

1 Cincinnati baseball team
2 Reserved
3 Main bread ingredient
4 Storm
5 Swine
6 Wharf
7 Unclip
8 Hydrochloric and sulfuric, for ex.
9 Surround
10 By way of
11 Note taker
12 Computer picture button
13 Alley
21 Take to court
23 Humble
26 Special menus
28 Expression of surprise
30 __ Lanka
31 Organized crime
33 Give
34 Had known
35 Treaty organization
36 Adam's garden
37 Admiral's authority
39 Vertical line
41 Water radar
42 Pro
45 Poet Edgar Allen
47 Pure quartz
50 French "yes"
52 Unconscious states
53 Cheep
55 Lamenting poem
56 Happen again
57 Mists
58 Hello!
60 Austin novel
61 Eat sparingly
63 Biblical "you"
65 Body of water
67 Disks

PUZZLE 18

ACROSS
1 Post-traumatic stress disorder
5 Forte
10 Cosmic
14 Bible book
15 In the ___, person
16 Notion
17 Off-Broadway award
18 Raccoon-like animal
19 Excuse me!
20 Seduce
22 Ragu's competition
24 Sixth sense
25 Small bunch of flowers
27 Movies
29 Better
32 Belgian Congo
35 Belt up
38 North by east
39 Worked as a waiter
40 Less than two
41 Cooked
43 Electroencephalograph (abbr.)
44 Gain interest
46 Slide on snow
47 Island
48 Capital of Senegala
49 Chicken brand
51 Had
54 Popinjay
57 Compose
59 Trample
62 __ acid
64 Capital of Western Samoa
66 Ancient German letters
68 Plateau
69 Loan
70 Eight
71 Flat
72 Sego lily's bulb
73 Full of swamp grass
74 Dried-up

DOWN
1 Secret plan
2 Hoses
3 Work carelessly
4 Ruby (2 wds.)
5 College football conference (abbr.)
6 Swill
7 Parch
8 Painter Richard
9 Upper leg
10 By way of
11 Glues
12 Observes with eye
13 Tap in lightly
21 Dickens' Tiny __
23 Seeped
26 Literature
28 Fight
30 BB association
31 Freethinker
33 Rotate
34 Adjoin
35 Cowboy boot projection
36 Ancient Indian
37 Determining
39 Quake
41 Charred
42 Air
45 Half-baked
47 Payoffs
50 Klutz
52 Inaccuracy
53 Two
55 Pain reliever brand
56 Smarter
57 Two good friends
58 Fencing sword
60 Wager
61 Accomplishment
63 Walking stick
65 Hoopla
67 Eye infection

PUZZLE 19

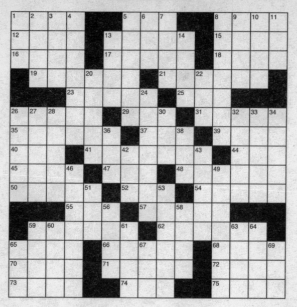

ACROSS

1 U.S. Department of Agriculture
5 Disks
8 Traveled by car
12 Mr. Donahue
13 Played a movie
15 Flat
16 Hawk
17 Chocolate tree
18 Rivalry
19 Sour ale
21 Claws
23 Ladies' counterparts
25 She
26 Speak suddenly
29 Adjust
31 Leaves out
35 Cowboy author Louis
37 Leather worker's tool
39 Coke
40 Bolus
41 House animal edibles (2 wds.)
44 Communication Workers of America (abbr.)
45 Gets older
47 Duet
48 Loaf of bread
50 Crimes
52 Received
54 Lasses
55 Fat
57 Decoration
59 Type of wheel
62 Ruler
65 Indonesian island
66 Craze
68 Be unsuccessful
70 Tactic
71 Strength
72 Pretend
73 Cutting tools
74 Large computer co.
75 Canal

DOWN

1 Highs
2 Popular stadium
3 Pickle herb
4 Fast (music term)
5 Maps
6 Medical practitioner
7 Hit
8 Changes
9 Baker's need
10 __ ex machina
11 The __ (final word)
13 Look over
14 Prophet who built the arc
20 Stand (2 wds.)
22 Sign of the zodiac
24 Caviar
26 Swollen
27 One of the Florida Keys
28 Deep brown
30 Couple
32 Accumulate debt
33 Shower need
34 Bats at a fly
36 Crimson
38 Throw
42 Pull
43 Chief ancient Philistine god
46 Yarns
49 Long-necked animal
51 Mr.
53 Boredom
56 Leg
58 Greenish-blue color
59 Imitation
60 Otherwise
61 Japanese dress
63 France & Germany river
64 Carved Polynesian pendant
65 Lingerie
67 Seize
69 Downwind

PUZZLE 20

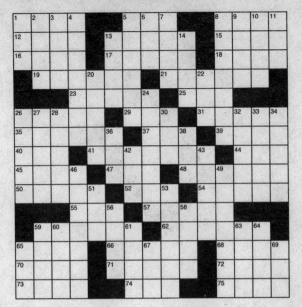

ACROSS
1 Fuel
5 Part of a min.
8 Roman Catholic church head
12 Curve
13 Humor
15 Brews
16 Mexican sandwich
17 Mountainous
18 Male
19 Winnow
21 Shallow pond
23 Diner
25 Affirmative gesture
26 Encomium
29 Weep
31 Capital of Bangladesh
35 Refer indirectly
37 Unrefined metal
39 Glided
40 I want my ___
41 Dole
44 Build up

45 Hurt
47 "To the right!"
48 Medicine from a plant
50 Malicious burning
52 Make a mistake
54 Type of Catholic
55 Disallow
57 Dried up
59 Spanish explorer
62 Played (2 wds.)
65 Join
66 Computer characters
68 Golf tournament
70 Bulb flower
71 Judged
72 Traditional knowledge
73 Shut up
74 Brew
75 Have knowledge

DOWN
1 Dab
2 Epochs
3 Account (abbr.)
4 Henry David ___
5 Glints
6 Elver
7 Jail room
8 Temples
9 Tub spread
10 Pennsylvania (abbr.)
11 Time zone
13 Voucher for a small debt
14 Baseball's Nolan
20 Root beer brand (3 wds.)
22 Deity
24 Shinglers
26 Grassy plain
27 Marriage site
28 Rock and Roll "King"
30 Lingerie
32 Ask for legally

33 Approximate date
34 Advertiser
36 Electroen-cephalograph (abbr.)
38 Time period
42 Downwind
43 Goofed
46 Most dignified
49 Virginia city
51 Seize
53 Re-employ
56 Prophet who built the arc
58 Surprise attack
59 Pierce
60 Related
61 At sea
63 On
64 Roman emperor
65 Shrill bark
67 Calorie
69 Latest

PUZZLE 21

ACROSS
1 Well done!
6 Musical treble __
10 Air (prefix)
14 France's "Sun King"
15 National capital
16 Muffin ingredient
17 Ocular
18 Decorative needle case
19 Saucer
20 Corporate top dog
21 Beehive State
23 Maladroit
25 Svelte
26 New York City
27 Snooze
30 Add sugar
34 Superior
35 Booted
36 By way of
38 World map
39 Goose egg
40 Raccoon-like animal
42 Japanese money
43 Jetty
44 Complete
45 Chits
48 Lubricators
49 Caustic substance
50 Artful
51 O.T. prophet in lion's den
54 French Sudan
55 Accountant
58 Swiss-like cheese
59 Do business
61 Mythological nymph
63 Coffee
64 Duke
65 Grind the teeth
66 Charge card
67 Removes the water
68 Got up

DOWN
1 Alliance
2 Strong cord
3 Cab
4 Roman numeral seven
5 Kiss
6 Whipped dairy food
7 Very reluctant
8 Flightless bird
9 Fictitious
10 Snatch
11 Little Mermaid's love
12 Thoughtless
13 One time
22 End
24 Popeye's yes
25 Prig
27 Sharp
28 More able
29 Cut of beef
30 Dickie
31 __ down
32 Circumvent
33 Gunpowder need
35 Breaking sound
37 Acquired Immune Deficiency Syndrome (abbr.)
40 Roofs
41 Simply
43 Used
46 Culminate
47 Peeper
48 Fat
50 Room dividers
51 __ vu
52 Eve's husband
53 Central church part
54 Christ's mother
55 Hello!
56 El __
57 Attention-Deficit Hyperactive Disorder (abbr.)
60 Serving of corn
62 Picnic pest

PUZZLE 22

ACROSS
1 1997 Madonna movie
6 Boyfriend
10 U.S. Department of Agriculture
14 Grant an extension
15 Make
16 Trudge
17 Afloat (2 wds.)
18 Mead
19 Canned meat
20 Drunkard
21 Movie star
23 Chemical compound
25 On top
26 Compass point
27 Elect (2 wds.)
30 Meter
34 Cook's garb
35 Skins
36 Grows acorns
38 Smarted
39 Wrath
40 Promised
42 Truss
43 Evils
44 Chili con __
45 Rudely
48 Armor plate
49 Duet
50 Cur
51 Look closely
54 September (abbr.)
55 Animal foot
58 European monetary unit
59 Egg-shaped
61 Shift
63 Prego's competition
64 Type of organ
65 Opposite of ally
66 Potato sprouts
67 Soothe
68 Idiots

DOWN
1 Epochs
2 Oppose
3 Institution (abbr.)
4 Ball holder
5 Expecting
6 Jazz
7 Duke
8 Is
9 Relaxes
10 North of downtown
11 Ghetto
12 Ended
13 Jewish calendar month
22 Put on
24 South by east
25 Long time
27 Cosmic
28 Ocular
29 Not as false
30 Permed
31 Greek god of war
32 Beer brand
33 Merits
35 Stuff
37 Joint
40 Scurried
41 Stay
43 Different forms of an element
46 Abominable
47 Star
48 Coffee holder
50 Scrimmage
51 Dried-up
52 Wharf
53 Goad
54 Drains sap
55 Secondary
56 Vertex
57 Reasons
60 By way of
62 Card game

PUZZLE 23

ACROSS
1 Canned chili brand
6 Hertz
9 Water (Sp.)
13 Store passageway
14 Is
15 Looking at
16 Drive away
17 Crimson
18 Eagle's nest
19 A cozy room (2 wds.)
20 Wishing
22 Type of partnership
23 New York City
24 Border
25 Donkey
27 Basic beliefs
29 Forever
33 Aurora
34 Nervous system
35 Ritual
36 Right angle to a ships length

39 Cooking vessel
40 Motorbike
41 Desire
42 Papa
43 Evergreen tree
44 Menace
46 Beginning
49 Cube
50 Deer relative
51 Change color
53 Sleeping place
56 Cloth
58 Italian currency
59 Keen
61 Tax agency
62 Permissions to enter foreign countries
63 Not our
64 Central Intelligence Agency
65 Repent
66 Tights
67 State
68 Campers dwellings

DOWN
1 Plastic wrap
2 Like hippie's clothing
3 Characteristic
4 Bottoms
5 Hair stuff
6 Rebound
7 Secondary
8 Dregs
9 Popeye's yes
10 Woman
11 Section
12 Elderly
15 National bird
20 Boo
21 Loony
24 Dining or living ending
26 Inaccuracies
28 Agitated
30 Snip
31 Snacked
32 Headed
34 Policeman
36 Boxer Muhammad

37 Tramp
38 Sixth sense
39 Debates
40 Fur
42 .16 of an inch
43 __ lore
45 Traveler
47 Phonograph inventor
48 Czar
50 Written material
52 Comforts
53 Clean
54 Reverberate
55 Fees
57 Opera solo
58 Diet
60 Truss
62 Tub

PUZZLE 24

ACROSS

1 Snow heavily
6 Typing rate
9 U.S. Department of Agriculture
13 African country
14 Caesar's three
15 Winder
16 Quell
17 Last month of year
18 Sacred song
19 Agenda
20 Jewish food
22 Pod vegetable
23 Adjust
24 Jigsaw
25 Great
27 Deepness
29 Legacy recipient
33 Moved quickly
34 Digit
35 Adolescent
36 Constituent
39 Lad
40 Hot liquid burn
41 Mind
42 Seize
43 Morse code dash
44 Queues (2 wds.)
46 African country
49 Points
50 Less than two
51 Expression of surprise
53 Computer part
56 Takes by force
58 Gall
59 Boat
61 Downwind
62 Commander of "Deep Space Nine"
63 God of Islam
64 Serving of corn
65 Nighttime images
66 Spruce
67 Resort hotel
68 Religious divisions

DOWN

1 Hits
2 Cultivated
3 Lay monastery dweller
4 Baseball's Nolan
5 Summer month
6 Black poisonous spider
7 Filled crusts
8 Beer type
9 Highs
10 Cleaning agent
11 Pineapple brand
12 __ matter
15 Small bunch of flowers
20 Genghis __
21 Fencing sword
24 Celebrity
26 Attractive
28 Hunted
30 Thirst quencher
31 Elver
32 The __ (final word)
34 Bath
36 Volume (abbr.)
37 Kimono sash
38 X
39 Small cases
40 Wise
42 Loony
43 Fox holes
45 Not north
47 3.26 light-years
48 Felix (2 wds.)
50 Musical production
52 Tiny particles
53 Greenish-blue color
54 Color deficient
55 Ca. University
57 Harvest
58 Cook pottery
60 Head apparel
62 Disks

PUZZLE 25

ACROSS

1 Punitive
6 Organization concerned with civil liberties (abbr.)
10 Swiss-like cheese
14 Short monster
15 Tribe
16 Portend
17 One-celled organism
18 Brand of milk
19 Life histories
20 Sausage
22 French Sudan
24 BB association
25 Wealthy man
27 Adult insect
29 Shedding outer layer
32 Rate
33 Constrictor snake
34 Setting
37 Bunsen burner
41 Radar target
43 Boxer Muhammad
44 Grain
45 Girdle
46 Peeved
48 Place
49 That (possessive)
51 French grammatical mark
54 Relating to the sun
56 Pay
57 Skit
58 Baby's "ball"
60 Metal paint
64 W
66 Canal
68 Suppress
69 Tub spread
70 End
71 Peals
72 Harp
73 Notion
74 Eight

DOWN

1 Parent teacher groups
2 Writer Bombeck
3 Christmas carol
4 Capital of New York
5 South American animals
6 Air Cushion Vehicle (abbr.)
7 Hike a mountain
8 Volcanic rock
9 Not similar
10 Move away
11 Executing
12 Philippine dish with marinated chicken or pork
13 Plateau
21 Wading bird
23 Pixy
26 Sesame Street's grouch
28 Excuse me!
29 Tides
30 Pop
31 Pulpit
35 Deer relative
36 Sibling's daughter
38 Duck
39 Nab
40 __ matter
42 Mr. Donahue
46 Hebrew
47 Districts of ancient Attica
50 Charge
52 Money
53 Slanted font
54 What a snake skin is
55 Finned mammal
56 Hoist
57 Truant
59 Nail
61 Coin
62 Adjoin
63 For fear that
65 Digit
67 Estimated time of arrival

PUZZLE 26

ACROSS

1 Plasma
6 Parts of plays
10 The alphabet
14 Capital of Japan
15 Fashionable
16 German "Mrs."
17 Ran out
18 Swerve
19 Small shed
20 State capital
22 Change
24 Rate
25 Expression of regret
27 Nautical "friend"
29 Dinner tool
32 Pastry
33 Snip
34 Chatty
37 Far away
41 Bulb flower
43 Beg
44 Grainery
45 Technical
46 Unmarried
48 San Diego attraction
49 Sign language
51 Became electrically charged
54 Lame
56 Rage
57 Newsman Rather
58 Association (abbr.)
60 Elicited
64 Payable
66 Sound of relief
68 Senile
69 Vegetable
70 Women's magazine
71 Concentrated
72 Fable
73 Lazy
74 Viper

DOWN

1 Post-traumatic stress disorder
2 Run easily
3 Related
4 Abounding in woods
5 Hotels
6 Air Cushion Vehicle (abbr.)
7 Face part
8 Even
9 Sparingly
10 College football conference (abbr.)
11 Bust
12 Cartoon character
13 Canal name
21 Pour
23 Thai
26 Tidy up
28 What Celestial Seasonings makes
29 Section
30 Exhaust
31 Great
35 West southwest
36 Bundle of yarn
38 Foam
39 Healing plant
40 Crucifix
42 Pillow covering
46 Odyssey Traveler
47 Former magistrate of Venice
50 Resort hotel
52 Silver State
53 Smooth
54 Ungainly
55 Inanimate
56 __ Saxon
57 Ordain
59 Window ledge
61 Considerate
62 Otherwise
63 Elk's cousin
65 Morse code dash
67 Carve

PUZZLE 27

ACROSS
1 Speak without preparation
6 Dog food brand
10 Stacked mattresses
14 Wake up
15 Severe
16 Afresh
17 Incite (2 wds.)
18 Looked
19 Prefix ten
20 Appear
21 Child
23 Mama
24 Swiss-like cheese
26 Egyptian paper (plural)
28 Abbreviate (abbr.)
31 Ballet skirt
32 Summer month
33 Gems carved in relief
36 Nails
40 School subject
42 Bullfight cheer

43 Snare
44 Tub spread
45 Plainly
48 Boxer Muhammad
49 Religious group
51 Verse meter
53 E. China tree
56 TV award
57 Vane direction
58 Powwow
61 Rodents
65 Brews
67 Definite
68 Afloat (2 wds.)
69 Cincinnati baseball team
70 Great
71 Layers
72 Eye infection
73 September (abbr.)
74 Thousands of sheets of paper

DOWN
1 Greek god of war
2 Former magistrate of Venice
3 Toboggan
4 Chemical compound
5 TV lawyer Matlock
6 Right angle to a ships length
7 "You can't eat just one" brand
8 V.P.'s boss
9 Sophocles' doomed protagonist
10 Unpleasant
11 Opposite of ally
12 Decoration
13 Religious teacher
21 Volcanic rock
22 Munch
25 Last month of year
27 Parlay
28 Bullets
29 False bible god
30 Computer

memory unit
31 Has toed
34 Trench
35 Wing
37 Middle East dweller
38 Indonesian island
39 __ and span
41 Prison
45 Women's shirts
46 Flavor of sherbet
47 Root vegetable
50 Expression
52 Shiny evergreen
53 What you shift
54 Cove
55 Homeless
56 Make a choice
59 Delude
60 Leaky faucet noise
62 East
63 Swarm
64 Back talk
66 South southeast
68 Rainy month

PUZZLE 28

ACROSS

1 Expression
6 Movie star
10 Omelette need
14 Half man, half goat
15 Prow
16 Region
17 Tilt
18 Pop
19 Layer
20 Cuts off "in the bud"
21 Dawn
23 Cubic centimeter
24 Soviet Union
26 National capital
28 Parallelograms
31 Signal
32 Fall mo.
33 Spring holiday
36 Opp. of starboard
40 Goose egg
42 Possess
43 Harvard's rival
44 Adam's garden

45 Having big choppers
48 Visit
49 Small city
51 Large body of water
53 Chant
56 Kill
57 River (Spanish)
58 Character on "Seinfeld"
61 What kids do
65 Hormone
67 Soft cheese from Greece
68 Swiftly
69 Siamese
70 Star __
71 Reddish dye
72 Snaky fish
73 Where a family lives
74 Viper

DOWN

1 Association (abbr.)
2 Painter of melting clocks
3 On top
4 Mineral
5 Bard's before
6 Accumulate debt
7 Entry
8 Capital of Norway
9 Pupil
10 Serving of corn
11 Fairy Tale writing brothers
12 Magic lamp dweller
13 Not happily
21 East
22 Cause of sickness
25 South by east
27 Unite
28 Tear down
29 Colored
30 Giant
31 Cabana

34 Anon
35 Couple
37 Soothe
38 Tiny insect
39 Adolescent
41 Upon
45 Last preteen birthday
46 Compel to go
47 Yes
50 Less than two
52 Cheated
53 Furious
54 Inglenook
55 Sum
56 Adder
59 Air (prefix)
60 Detail
62 Ground
63 Teen disease
64 52 weeks
66 Possessive pronoun
68 Expression of surprise

PUZZLE 29

ACROSS

1 Wing
4 Half man, half goat
9 Lazy __ (turn table)
14 Direct
15 Adios
16 Male relative
17 Mountain Standard Time
18 Hair care product brand
19 Footwear
20 Popular stadium
22 Lazy people
24 Kid
25 Resort hotel
27 Fat
29 One of the N. and S. States
32 Snatch
35 Label
36 Computer screen dot
38 Widely known
40 Replace a striker
42 Cuban,' for example
44 Harvard's rival
45 Vial
47 Harmonize
49 What's owed
50 Yearly
52 Swamp
54 Tricky
55 Cake or Bread ___
56 American Cancer Society (abbr.)
59 Tenant
63 Tryout
67 Dance
69 Foot sores
71 Slide on snow
72 Hike a mountain
73 Life and __
74 Fasten
75 Shoddy
76 Forest clearing
77 North northeast

DOWN

1 Weapons
2 Sappy
3 Wager
4 Exhaust
5 Sea near Italy
6 Even
7 Shriek
8 Law
9 Lessen
10 Card game
11 Scotsman
12 Singing voice
13 Bird's home
21 Beg
23 Hustle
26 Papa
28 I Love __ (tv show)
29 Country house
30 Once more
31 Lengthwise
32 Fright
33 Cover
34 Debris at the base of a cliff
35 Teaspoon (abbr.)
37 Chick holder
39 Ball holder
41 Prohibits
43 Resumed business again
46 Child's song
48 Time period
51 Popeye's yes
53 Picnic pest
56 Account (abbr.)
57 Pop
58 Irritation
60 Acting (abbr.)
61 Sully
62 Writer Bombeck
64 Sports channel
65 Pare
66 Prong
68 Time zone
70 South southeast

PUZZLE 30

ACROSS

1 Shape
4 Seasoned rice
9 Unit of electric capacitance
14 Poem
15 Adios
16 Type of glue
17 Close to the ground
18 Giver
19 Dickens' "__ of Two Cities" (2 wds.)
20 Removes the water
22 Microscope viewers
24 Crimson
25 Killed in action
27 Snacked
29 Blin
32 Pick up
35 French "yes"
36 Creed
38 Funeral hymn
40 Island

42 Stories
44 Labels
45 Trickle
47 Type of mob
49 Kid
50 Observers
52 Fragrances
54 North by east
55 Respect
56 By way of
59 Cat toy stuffing
63 Reasons
67 Large Asian nation
69 Eagle's nest
71 Sports official
72 Sell
73 Behavior
74 Farm credit administration (abbr.)
75 Dukes
76 Island nation
77 Distant

DOWN

1 Headstrong
2 Aroma
3 Moist
4 Wrestling mat
5 Idol worship
6 Straight mark
7 Long time
8 Skins
9 Ate large meal
10 Inclined
11 Menacing animal noise
12 Shaft
13 Tinted
21 Slide on snow
23 Serving of corn
26 Business abbr.
28 Change
29 Public transportation vehicles
30 Spring flower
31 Enthusiasms
32 Title of Italian woman
33 Non __

34 Kellogg's waffles
35 Fat
37 Dull
39 Time zone
41 Economics abrv.
43 Scratching
46 Wheel parts
48 In what way
51 Thirst quencher
53 Kitten's cry
56 Gripping tool
57 Ancient Indian
58 Jewish calendar month
60 27th U.S. president
61 Roman emperor
62 Flatten
64 "I'll __ and I'll puff..."
65 Young Men's Christian Association
66 Fence
68 Peaked
70 Estimated time of arrival

PUZZLE 31

ACROSS

1 Tangle
4 Measuring instrument
8 Assembled
14 Less than two
15 Invalid
16 Liveliness
17 Danish krone (abbr.)
18 Particle
19 Portuguese governess
20 One who chooses
22 Time period
23 Plateau
24 GS
27 Singing parts
31 Tropical edible root
33 For
35 Pride
36 Imp
38 Snip
39 Organization concerned with civil liberties (abbr.)
40 Exhaustedly
44 Book bag
46 A cozy room (2 wds.)
47 Cation
49 Oodles
50 Downwind
51 Chance
52 What a clock tells
55 Islam's head
58 Economics (abbr.)
61 Airway
63 Visit
65 Remembrance gift
67 Disputer
70 Type of organ
71 Morse code dot
72 Open square
73 Celebrity
74 Bard's before
75 Scoundrels
76 Island
77 Rock group

DOWN

1 Electronic equipment
2 Ankle bracelet
3 Mother __
4 Tiny insect
5 Cars
6 Old __ (US flag)
7 Tree
8 Caused
9 Sporty car brand
10 Creep away
11 Goof
12 Long time
13 Genetic code
21 Tilt
25 Licensed practical nurse
26 Bulb flower
28 Technical
29 Eye
30 Spirit
32 Olden
34 Opaque gem
37 Dart
39 Not dormant
40 Baby powder
41 Notion
42 Rotate
43 Past times
45 Kid
48 New York City
53 Maintenance man
54 Total
56 Car manufacturer
57 Hard impact
59 Leaves out
60 Asian country
62 Emblem
64 Epochs
66 Bare
67 Rainy mo.
68 River (Spanish)
69 Quip
70 Pounds per square inch

PUZZLE 32

ACROSS

1 American Cancer Society (abbr.)
4 Central church part
8 Remove by surgery
14 Papa
15 Wading bird
16 Hockey position
17 BB association
18 Male
19 Asian nation
20 Terrestrial
22 Second to last month
23 As well as
24 Otherwise
27 Jewish bread
31 Technical
33 For
35 With it
36 Distress call
38 Shrill bark
39 Quote
40 Ref
44 Acceptable principle
46 King of beasts
47 Talk
49 Caustic substance
50 Ship initials
51 Fall mo.
52 Cliff
55 Holy city
58 Christmas
61 Prune
63 Hoopla
65 Banned
67 Famous female pilot, Earhart
70 U.S. Department of Agriculture
71 Estimated time of arrival
72 Tom __
73 Bottoms
74 Gain
75 Network
76 Not there
77 Ball holder

DOWN

1 Sleep disorder
2 Element
3 Scarce
4 At hand
5 White poplar
6 Plastic
7 Time zone
8 Against
9 Chest
10 Maggot
11 Wing
12 Truss
13 Elver
21 Warning signal
25 Snoop
26 Little Mermaid's love
28 Skinny
29 Pasta
30 Organization of Petroleum Exporting Countries
32 Stolen
34 Opaque gem

37 Sego lily's bulb
39 Force
40 Short for aluminum
41 Heave
42 Pear type
43 Risque
45 New York City
48 Heat unit
53 Silvery
54 Small pointed beard
56 Sepals of a flower
57 Adios
59 Smooth tightly twisted thread
60 Old
62 Eating dish
64 Rowers needs
66 Alley
67 Poisonous snake
68 Bad (prefix)
69 Ram's mate
70 Expression

PUZZLE 33

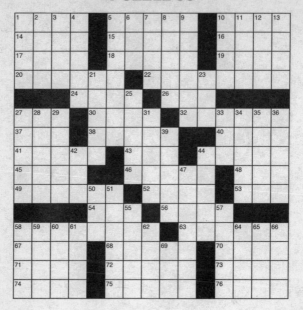

ACROSS

1 Male deer
5 Deteriorate
10 Not that
14 Curve
15 Iranian's neighbor
16 Lurk
17 Bod
18 Swagger
19 Not many (2 wds.)
20 Laughing dogs
22 South pacific islander
24 Competition at the Greek games
26 X
27 Snacked
30 Prayer ending
32 Cola brand
37 Candle element
38 Dallas denizen
40 Nerve fiber
41 Having wings
43 United States of America
44 Being deceitful
45 Law
46 Not happily
48 New Jersey's neighbor
49 Revere
52 King of beasts
53 Bard's before
54 Touch an animal
56 Speed
58 West Indies location
63 Felix (2 wds.) .
67 Movie star
68 Luck o' the __
70 Prego's competition
71 Central church part
72 Long boat
73 Flatten
74 Sketched
75 What an animal does
76 Adjoin

DOWN

1 Girdle
2 Helen of __
3 Vertex
4 African country
5 Limber
6 Creative work
7 Separate
8 Stumpy
9 Goes with or
10 Not this
11 Hi-fi
12 Notion
13 Stitched together
21 Multi-colored rock
23 Business abbr.
25 Bond
27 Informed
28 Debris at the base of a cliff
29 Glorify
31 Whining voice type
33 Coral reef
34 Carbon mon__
35 Individualist

36 Slant
39 Lowest point
42 Ball holder
44 Type of mob
47 Abhors
50 Environmental protection agency (abbr.)
51 Doctors
55 Jewish scripture
57 Spooky
58 Hogtie
59 Jewish calendar month
60 Range
61 Fanned
62 Cosecant's opposite
64 Tease
65 Excited
66 Adjust
69 Sward

PUZZLE 34

ACROSS

1 Cheats
5 Capital of Oregon
10 Actor Alda
14 Stray
15 Texas stew
16 Science channel
17 Malaria
18 Has ears
19 Trigger
20 Flick with the fingers
22 Aggravate
24 Carry
26 Yes
27 South southeast
30 Egyptian river
32 Dusky
37 Black tie
38 Frosting
40 Fancy car
41 Jell-o salad
43 Fox hole
44 Quell
45 Ruined
46 Electronic mail
48 Maturity
49 Boos
52 Young Women's Christian Association
53 Common fish
54 African antelope
56 Father
58 Snake killing animal
63 Hose
67 Opera solo
68 Indian money
70 Region
71 Southeast by south
72 Braid
73 Undertaking
74 Hospital (abbr.)
75 Spectacles
76 Otherwise

DOWN

1 Tennis player Steffi
2 Yoga practicer
3 Pope John ___
4 Soft-finned fish
5 Cynic
6 Expression of surprise
7 Italian currency
8 Lamenting poem
9 Pygmy
10 Opposed
11 Traditional knowledge
12 Tel ___ (Israel's capital)
13 Neck
21 Type of Greek column
23 Half-baked
25 Suppress
27 Hoard
28 Japanese dish
29 Big exhibits
31 Opposite of ally
33 Peaked
34 Spring flower
35 Adult insect
36 Played
39 Chew like a rodent
42 That (possessive)
44 Wing shaped
47 Frostiness
50 Pride
51 Inhales loudly
55 Arrogate
57 Thrill
58 Mush
59 Brand of sandwich cookie
60 Small licorice treats
61 Puff
62 Fencing sword
64 Spoken
65 Loch ___ monster
66 One's good
69 Escudo

PUZZLE 35

ACROSS
1 Can
5 Like a wing
9 Goad
13 Bone
14 Mustang
15 Hour
16 Docile
17 Top level
18 Staff
19 City
21 Inclining
23 Insightful
25 Otherwise
26 Been
29 Removes the water
31 Book of facts
34 Skit
35 Gyroscopes
37 Declines
39 Sculpt
41 Time period
42 Pancake need
43 South American nation
44 Small Mediterranean boat
46 Flightless bird
47 Dales
50 Do it again
51 Fox hole
52 Prick
54 Revel
56 Both lane driver (2 wds)
59 Newly washed window blemish
63 Government (abbr.)
64 "Remember the __ "
66 Bunsen burner
67 Fencing sword
68 Hot sandwich
69 Hormone
70 Fix
71 Association (abbr.)
72 Skinny

DOWN
1 Acting (abbr.)
2 Nail
3 Dalai __
4 Better
5 Creative work
6 Gobs
7 Senile
8 Cola brand
9 Awkward to carry
10 Colored horse
11 Chinese chime
12 The __ (final word)
14 Bread factory
20 Grassy marsh plant
22 Pacific Standard Time
24 Glass kitchenware
26 Hornet
27 Hurt
28 Gaze
30 In more pain
32 Uttered
33 Froth
36 Sword
38 Made a web
40 Contracted rhythmically
42 Scud
45 Phonograph inventor
48 Type of partnership
49 Famous desert
53 Orb
55 Give a present
56 Strong cord
57 Baker's need
58 Scads
60 __-a-sketch
61 Opposed
62 Genghis __
63 Pearl
65 Women's partners

PUZZLE 36

ACROSS

1 Pulls
5 Canal
9 Passing trends
13 Capital of Norway
14 Rainbow maker
15 Tub spread
16 Shallow area
17 Jagged
18 Garret
19 Had a dream
21 Jailer
23 Sully
25 Id's counterparts
26 Damage
29 Parent teacher groups
31 Cain's eldest son
34 Ram's mate
35 Spooky
37 Prophet who built the arc
39 Mythological nymph
41 Nettle
42 Ancient Greek marketplace
43 Goad
44 Relating to birds
46 Pacific Standard Time
47 Result
50 Decorative needle case
51 Her
52 Russian ruler
54 Store
56 Directed
59 Respire
63 Teen disease
64 Lading
66 At sea
67 Smooth
68 Expression
69 Chasm
70 Sticky fastener
71 Cheats
72 Oils

DOWN

1 Male aristocrat
2 Exploiter
3 Gaiety
4 Couches
5 Make a mistake
6 Revel
7 Supply
8 Show up
9 Culture music
10 Healing plant
11 Resist
12 Drunkard
14 Wee
20 Motorbike
22 Not (refix)
24 Maggot
26 List of meals
27 Informed
28 Rule
30 Strain
32 Cooperatives (hyp.)
33 Stern
36 Leaves
38 Detest
40 Person sensitive to art
42 Negatively charged particle
45 Preoccupation
48 Avail
49 Flying insect
53 It's done
55 Dock
56 Ca. University
57 Breaking sound
58 Leaky faucet noise
60 East
61 Opp. of starboard
62 Dines
63 American Federation of Teachers (abbr.)
65 Aurora

PUZZLE 37

ACROSS

1 Chinese cooking pan
4 Staple
9 Monkey
12 Region
14 Musical production
15 Assure
16 Was looked at
17 Stomach sore
18 Prong
19 Knows many languages
21 __ and Company
23 Rock group
24 Bad (prefix)
25 Hindu goddess, consort of Siva
28 Constrictor snake
31 Post-traumatic stress disorder
34 Computer phones
36 Contagious disease
38 For
40 Section
41 Mischievous
43 __ Piper
44 Last month of year
45 Snacked
46 Painter Georgia __
48 Decorative needle case
51 Mr..'s wife
53 Orient
54 Papa
56 Abridged (abbr.)
58 Capital of Montana
61 Ovate
66 Against
67 Eskimo home
69 Duke
70 No longer for sale
71 Synthetic fiber
72 Triad
73 Pacific Standard Time
74 Use money
75 Sixth sense

DOWN

1 Hornet
2 Brand of sandwich cookie
3 Careen
4 Greek government
5 Composure
6 Religious division
7 Wrath
8 Rebound
9 Tel __ (Israel's capital)
10 Cornmeal cake
11 Pitcher
13 One of these
15 Tipped
20 Stern
22 Lick
25 Recipient
26 Decree
27 Ex-serviceman
29 Suggest
30 Boxer Muhammad
32 Double agents
33 Laundry detergent brand
34 Clay
35 Body of water
37 Card game
39 Poem
42 Long-term memory
43 Pod vegetable
47 Lotion brand
49 Turn over
50 Cation
52 Western bar
55 Hurts
57 Flaxen
58 Fastener
59 Id's counterparts
60 Gait
61 Women's magazine
62 Touch an animal
63 Weight of a container
64 Bulb flower
65 Horse's walking sound
68 Con

PUZZLE 38

ACROSS

1 Melancholy
4 Better
9 Poisonous snake
12 Capital of Western Samoa
14 Small knife
15 Rascal
16 Retain
17 Speak
18 Ventilates
19 Removes
21 Scared
23 Reporter's question
24 Microgram
25 Gripping tool
28 Umpire
31 Visionary
34 Decipher
36 Rock group
38 Electroencephalograph (abbr.)
40 Bulb flower
41 Crank
43 Partial
44 South southeast
45 Space
46 Where you go after death
48 Middle East dweller
51 School group
53 Prayer ending
54 Old-fashioned Fathers
56 Butane
58 First month of Jewish calendar
61 Boatman
66 Decorative needle case
67 Lawn
69 Yoga practicer
70 Won
71 Care for
72 Adam's garden
73 Rate
74 Brownness
75 Vane direction

DOWN

1 One's good
2 Cusp
3 Eat sparingly
4 Era
5 One who dies for a cause
6 Epochs
7 Gain
8 Nighttime images
9 Opera solo
10 Japanese dress
11 Post-traumatic stress disorder
13 Rainy mo.
15 Ship
20 Reverent
22 Farm credit administration (abbr.)
25 Vice __
26 Colder
27 Distress call
29 Explode
30 Female (abbr.)
32 Put through a hole
33 Asian nation
34 Pluto
35 Chick holder
37 Miles per hour
39 Card game
42 Type of music
43 Surface to air missile
47 Soothe
49 Louse
50 Saloon
52 Tennis player Andre
55 Roadway instructions
57 Afloat (2 wds.)
58 Wood
59 Annoying, like a bug bite
60 Canal name
61 Distort
62 Seed bread
63 Particular form
64 Gets older
65 Before ten
68 Regret

PUZZLE 39

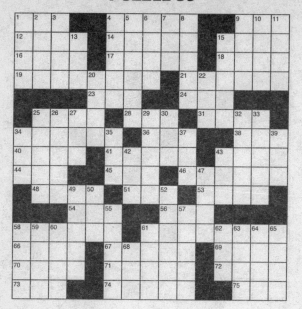

ACROSS

1 Representative
4 __ and pains
9 Communication Workers of America (abbr.)
12 Organization concerned with civil liberties (abbr.)
14 Intone
15 Cleaning agent
16 Thick carpet
17 Scholar
18 Goad
19 Hold pans
21 Chopped off
23 Make angry
24 Whiz
25 Christmas carol
28 Precedes an alias
31 Snare
34 Fruit
36 Advertisements
38 Make a mistake
40 Concluded
41 Drudge
43 Water (Sp.)
44 Average work performance
45 Pride
46 Loafing
48 Light
51 Move away
53 Soothe
54 Sixth sense
56 Snacked
58 Nova __
61 Hawaii climate
66 Frost
67 Large billed bird
69 Pop
70 Cab
71 What bears like
72 Orient
73 Miles per hour
74 __ Saxon
75 Digit

DOWN

1 File
2 Reverberate
3 Small ground plot
4 Performer
5 Buskin
6 Head coverings
7 Vane direction
8 Inscribed stone
9 Corporation (abbr.)
10 Payment
11 Copied
13 Expression
15 Excellent
20 Fatty
22 Fall mo.
25 Having to do with the navy
26 Musical production
27 Serving of corn
29 Barbecued stick
30 Hoopla
32 Plate armor
33 Clip
34 Papa
35 Brew
37 __ Lanka
39 Remnant
42 Maturity
43 Wing
47 Insightful
49 Subway
50 Pounds per square inch
52 Vessel
55 High ranking man-used formerly
57 Capital of Japan
58 Pillow covering
59 __ d'etat
60 Swearword
61 Chinese secret society
62 Winter hazard
63 Layer
64 As well as
65 Opp. of early
68 Large weight unit

PUZZLE 40

ACROSS
1 Ado
7 Beehive State
11 Environmental protection agency (abbr.)
14 Foray
15 Neck
16 Crony
17 Remove the bones
18 All-knowing
19 Unrefined metal
20 ___ Matisse, painter
22 Tonic
24 Drink slowly
27 Business abbr.
29 Saclike structures filled with fluid or diseased matter
30 Russian ruler
32 Decorum
35 Change into bone
37 Bod
38 Advertisements
41 Yield

42 Vinegar's acid
44 Downwind
45 Popular stadium
48 Curler
49 Assail
51 Spouse
52 Prick
55 Chance
56 Compass point
57 Misters
60 Spooky
64 Inclined
65 As well as
67 Lazy people
71 Visit
72 Pope John ___
73 Cheifs
74 She
75 Use a keyboard
76 Part of a coat

DOWN
1 Concealed
2 Less than two
3 Bolus
4 Winnie the ___
5 Alley
6 A cozy room (2 wds.)
7 Relaxes
8 Thai
9 Recess
10 Bottom
11 Type of glue
12 Fashion capital
13 Notify
21 River (Spanish)
23 Slippery frigid
24 Chair
25 Supply
26 Glue
28 Corporate top dog
31 Tear
32 Legends
33 Wise
34 Mexican sandwich
36 Flurry

38 Book of facts
39 Special menus
40 Turn
43 Tree
46 Munch
47 Halo
49 Abdominal muscles (abbr.)
50 Caustic substance
52 Break
53 Wigwam
54 Spring flower
58 Engrossed
59 Kill
61 Chest bones
62 Movie star
63 Otherwise
66 Eat
68 Vane direction
69 Pastor (abbr.)
70 South southeast

PUZZLE 41

ACROSS

1 Expression
7 Made music vocally
11 Parent
14 Dragger
15 Decorative needle case
16 Past
17 Lustrous
18 Cincinnati baseball team
19 Relation
20 Non __
22 Hydrocarbon
24 Resort hotel
27 Highs
29 Goad
30 Not bottom
32 Drain
35 Personal property
37 In __ (together)
38 Rainy mo.
41 Weaker
42 Dally
44 Eye infection
45 Cuts off "in the bud"
48 Dweller of the Beehive State
49 Repeat
51 Write down quickly
52 Made a web
55 Unrefined metal
56 Heifer
57 Bath powder
60 Root beer brand (3 wds.)
64 Curve
65 Make tight
67 Gully
71 Charge
72 Vale
73 Telephoned
74 Popular president's initials
75 Wager
76 Attach

DOWN

1 Accountant
2 Drag
3 Peaked
4 Fly
5 Judge
6 Writer Bombeck
7 Angels
8 Southwestern Indian
9 Naked
10 Essence
11 Capital of Senegala
12 Growing older
13 Recipient
21 Black tie
23 Hovel
24 Trunks
25 Suggest
26 Ably
28 State
31 Melancholy
32 Spooky
33 Unmerited
34 Get out!

36 Cabana
38 Special case only (2 wds.)
39 Greek philosopher
40 Grant an extension
43 Pallid
46 For
47 Bread brand (2 wds.)
49 Business abbr.
50 Thirst quencher
52 Workers
53 Peeled
54 Stomache sore
58 U.S. Department of Agriculture
59 Catty
61 Nothing
62 Leaky faucet noise
63 Cover a present
66 Alternative (abbr.)
68 Bullfight cheer
69 Japanese money
70 Cooky

PUZZLE 42

ACROSS

1 Bamboo bear
6 Crisp bread
10 Bad (prefix)
13 Decorates
15 After awhile
16 Pride
17 Cowboy shows
18 Antic
19 What a nurse gives
20 A cozy room (2 wds.)
22 Graphic description
24 Brand
26 Gets older
28 Superman's Ms. Lane
29 Accustomed
30 Country in SE Asia
31 Weight unit
32 Absent
33 Religious division
34 Reservoir

35 Patella
37 Caribe
41 Eat
42 One's good
43 Possessive pronoun
44 Crick
47 Double agent
48 Prow
49 Canned meat
50 Vegetable
51 Armored combat vehicle
52 Supplication
54 Brake
56 Cause of sickness
57 Lawmen
59 End
63 Card game
64 Canal
65 They make you an uncle
66 Drag
67 Sketched
68 Burial chamber

DOWN

1 Average work performance
2 Hoopla
3 Affirmative gesture
4 Had a dream
5 Positive electrode
6 Really cool
7 Fuses
8 Carbonated drinks
9 Door grip
10 Shooting star
11 One of the three graces
12 Cicada
14 South southeast
21 Colored People's association
23 South American animal
24 Sentence part
25 Wager
27 Received
29 Chinese cooking pan
30 Skip

31 Feel concern
33 Water film
34 Dam
36 Written material
37 Whitens from fear
38 Hour
39 Outer layer
40 Is
42 Sun's name
44 City in Minnesota (2 wds.)
45 Cat food brand
46 Type of watch
47 Black and white bird
48 Dozer
50 Seasoner makers
51 Harmful
53 Type of tea
55 X
58 Tailor
60 Slippery frigid
61 Representative
62 Time zone

PUZZLE 43

ACROSS

1 Squashed circles
6 Change
10 Marsh
13 Leg bone
15 Has no manners
16 Unrefined metal
17 Relating to the ankle bone
18 Tack
19 Hotel
20 Father
22 Bumpy
24 Pen fillers
26 Montana (abbr.)
28 Peter, for short
29 Notion
30 Pop
31 Goddess
32 Neither's partner
33 Ward off
34 European sea eagle
35 Final
37 Cajun
41 Central daylight time
42 Haze
43 __ Lanka
44 Nucleus
47 Northeast by north
48 Bend your arm
49 Band instrument
50 Central points
51 Guilty or not
52 Breath weapon
54 Formal "your"
56 Compact bundle
57 One time
59 Antenna
63 Estimated time of arrival
64 Competition at the Greek games
65 Took big steps
66 Sleeping place
67 What a clock tells
68 Governing group

DOWN

1 Often poetically
2 By way of
3 Abridged (abbr.)
4 National capital
5 Thick slices
6 Make a mistake
7 Portuguese governess
8 Dope
9 Babysit
10 Tank holding steam
11 Showy
12 Literature
14 Loose gown worn at mass
21 Amid
23 Turn over
24 Movie star
25 Roman emperor
27 Olden
29 Business abbr.
30 Penny
31 Cliff
33 Bona __
34 Economics abrv.
36 Turn
37 Limits
38 Island
39 Region
40 Nothing
42 Part of a min.
44 What a spider leaves
45 Remove by surgery
46 Thingumajig
47 Noncommissioned officer
48 Light snowfall
50 Mushrooms
51 Poetry writers
53 Kid's mom
55 In possession of
58 Vane direction
60 Cation
61 Hoopla
62 Headed

PUZZLE 44

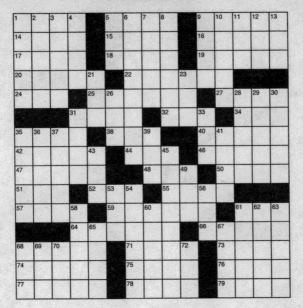

ACROSS
1 Clod
5 Svelte
9 Scent
14 At sea
15 Juno
16 Soap
17 Catty
18 Aegis
19 Wire
20 Protrude
22 Rate
24 Snoop
25 In the interior
27 Carved Polynesian pendant
31 Cafe
32 Charge
34 Crimson
35 Lotion brand
38 Snip
40 Capital of Japan
42 Pressers
44 Snip
46 Fish basket

47 Alleys
48 Wing
50 Totals
51 Acid
52 Pull
55 Duke
57 Long time
59 Ferocious
61 Time zone
64 Subclass including ticks and mites
66 Utter
68 Gas company
71 Notion
73 Jewish calendar month
74 Monte __
75 Vassal
76 Frau's husband
77 Clasp
78 Legion
79 __ Minor (Little Dipper)

DOWN
1 Baby sheep
2 Sap (2 wds.)
3 Grainy
4 Pain
5 Her
6 Rank below embassy
7 Luck o' the __
8 Geology
9 The alphabet
10 Cook with dry heat
11 Bolus
12 Bad (prefix)
13 Hatchet
21 Ram's mate
23 Vane direction
26 Peaked
28 Peeved
29 Made lock openers
30 Gods
31 Eat dinner
33 And so forth
35 "To __ Mockingbird" (2 wds.)

36 Efface
37 Musical piece
39 Pastry
41 Spoken
43 Fast plane
45 Beggars
49 Drag
53 United States of America
54 Gaudy
56 Pastor (abbr.)
58 What a hammer hits
60 Movie on tape
61 Bedspread feather
62 Former wounds
63 __ cotta (clay)
65 Horse's walking sound
67 Next to Kauai
68 Microgram
69 Paddle
70 Lingerie
72 American Federation of Teachers (abbr.)

PUZZLE 45

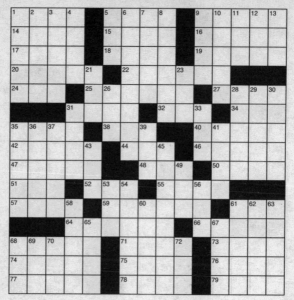

ACROSS

1 Deal a blow to
5 Russian ruler
9 Tendon
14 Military officer
15 Pound
16 Tight at the top, flaring at the bottom (2 wds.)
17 Tiny insect
18 Honey makers
19 Keyboard key next to "!"
20 Inch forward
22 Seasickness symptom
24 Regret
25 Church usher
27 Removes the water
31 Oracle
32 Ball holder
34 Cation
35 Hormone
38 Liberal (abbr.)
40 Strong drink
42 Tremble
44 Bolus
46 Lawn tool
47 Saudi Arabian citizen
48 Wing
50 Glen
51 Vane direction
52 Nervous system
55 Usages
57 Air (prefix)
59 Doughnut-shaped rolls
61 Munch
64 Ready-made structure
66 Hot __
68 Pope's governing organization
71 Famous cookies
73 Less than usual in size, power or character
74 Sturdy
75 Revel
76 Asian nation
77 Swarms
78 Murky
79 What the telephone did

DOWN

1 Stake
2 Eastern religion
3 Expression
4 Dole out
5 Charge
6 Plot outline
7 In the lead
8 Upshot
9 Satiate
10 Book by Homer
11 Goose egg
12 The __ (final word)
13 Bitty
21 South by east
23 Visit
26 Elver
28 Range of hills
29 Bumpkin
30 What an angry animal does
31 Booted
33 First woman
35 Afloat (2 wds.)
36 Tag

37 Not as false
39 Lingerie
41 Chances of winning
43 Pen brand
45 Price guide (2 wds.)
49 Sign language
53 North by east
54 Hunting expedition
56 Time zone
58 Narcotic
60 Charming tomboy
61 Swelling
62 Advertiser
63 Making a knot
65 Rodents
67 Aroma
68 Central Standard Time
69 Southwestern Indian
70 Seafood
72 Eye infection

PUZZLE 46

ACROSS

1 __ matter
5 Rice wine
9 Afresh
13 Layer
14 Small bunch of flowers
15 Rolled chocolate candy brand
16 Pain
17 Encomium
18 Russian ruler
19 Etc.
21 __ Express (train)
23 Saturate
24 Wading bird
25 Number used in multiplying
28 Brings in from the car
31 Dregs
32 Woolen cloth
34 Meshes
36 Sign language
37 Pride
38 Corporate top dog
39 __ down
41 Fusses
43 Monk's hood
44 Little Dipper handle star
46 Sandy
48 Band instrument
49 Trounce
50 Part human part machine
53 People from Faero Islands
57 Den
58 Indian corn
60 Baker's need
61 Women's magazine
62 Ethan that led the Green Mountain Boys
63 Germ
64 Join by heating
65 Require
66 Goofs

DOWN

1 Pound
2 Klutz
3 Artist Chagall
4 Verifies
5 Arc
6 Region
7 Killed in action
8 Not noble
9 Craftsman
10 Prow
11 Dash
12 Malt
14 Uses a pointed weapon
20 Also
22 River (Spanish)
24 Metal bar
25 Imperfection
26 Fable writer
27 Large stringed instrument
28 Suggests
29 Decoration
30 Boils
33 Spooky

35 Only
40 Dumbfounded
41 Underwater military person
42 Window covering
43 Rear train
45 Abridged (abbr.)
47 Possessive pronoun
49 Groggy
50 Inform
51 Harvard's rival
52 Notice of payment
53 Alphabetize documents
54 Always
55 Oracle
56 Ceases
59 Brew

PUZZLE 47

ACROSS

1 Hiking equipment
5 __ vu
9 Money
13 Shaft
14 Logarithm base
15 One time
16 Dalai __
17 Where you were at crime time
18 Secure
19 Gerbil (2 wds.)
21 Representatives
23 Raps lightly
24 Sleigh
25 Land mass
28 Dopier
31 Like a wing
32 Counterfeit
34 Inform
36 Eye infection
37 Sign of the zodiac
38 Stinger
39 Ride a horse
41 Computer input device

43 Range
44 One more
46 Melted
48 Menacing animal noise
49 Has toed
50 Kicked
53 Most jolly
57 Next to Kauai
58 Furious
60 Brand of sandwich cookie
61 Move while sleeping
62 Truck
63 TV award
64 Footwear
65 Young Women's Christian Association
66 Pulpit

DOWN

1 Guys' dates
2 Test
3 __ matter
4 House seller
5 Valleys
6 Change
7 Sail
8 Direction of an axis
9 ___ genius
10 After awhile
11 Scotsman
12 Not his
14 Knocked
20 Lick
22 Hair stuff
24 Game "__ Says"
25 Orient
26 Fanatical
27 Synthetic fabric
28 Smudge
29 Jostle
30 Put through a hole
33 Stomache sore
35 Unwanted plant

40 Agony
41 Suspiciously
42 Floor
43 Signaled by audio
45 Digit
47 She
49 Domestic fish
50 Hirer
51 Swearword
52 American state
53 Artist Chagall
54 Writer Bombeck
55 Partial
56 Children's love
59 Propel with oars

PUZZLE 48

ACROSS

1 File
5 Store passageway
10 Girdle
14 At sea
15 Origin
16 Quote
17 Playmate
19 Military unit
20 Elver
21 Soil
23 Heptad
26 Harsh
28 Winter hazard
31 Slide on snow
32 After seconds
33 Least amount
34 Cookie ingredient measurement
37 Trample
39 Fanned
40 Region
42 Adios
45 Social work duty
49 Wave
50 Walk fast
53 Roman numeral seven
54 Nervous system
55 Time segments
56 Poem
58 Herb
60 W.C.
61 Off-Broadway award
63 Insulting
69 List of names
70 Hoses
71 Canal
72 Bare scalp
73 Fatty vegetable
74 Department (abbr.)

DOWN

1 Type of music
2 Sign language
3 Body of water
4 Receiver
5 Cain killed him
6 Peaked
7 Sun's name
8 Raider
9 British King's name
10 Look over
11 Broadcasting period
12 Short-term memory
13 __ you! (attention getter)
18 Bog
22 Part in front of the ankle
23 Fast plane
24 Stretch to make do
25 By way of
26 Exhibit
27 Can metal
29 Central Intelligence Agency
30 The __ (final word)
32 Digit
35 South by east
36 Lush
38 Rodent
40 Totals
41 Seafood
42 College football conference (abbr.)
43 Newsman Rather
44 Impart gradually
45 Sky
46 __ league school
47 Fat
48 Goose egg
51 Vegetable
52 Remorseful
56 Cation
57 Adored
59 Had
60 Fail to keep
61 Bolus
62 Constrictor snake
64 National police
65 Pastor (abbr.)
66 Wrath
67 Snip
68 Fetch

PUZZLE 49

ACROSS

1 Sew together
5 Hesitation
10 Scoop
14 Island
15 Inch forward
16 Simply
17 Subscribers
19 Compel to go
20 Make angry
21 Belgian Congo
23 Pie nut
26 Fad
28 Traveler's aid
31 Teaspoon (abbr.)
32 Relating to the brain
33 Wrath
34 Roman marvel
37 Found
39 Fable
40 Amiss
42 Strength
45 Partial moon shape
49 Seafood
50 Humble
53 Neither's partner
54 Abridged (abbr.)
55 Hazes
56 Pater
58 Gods
60 Throng
61 Kill
63 Oils
69 Floor covering
70 Sandwich cookies brand
71 Soft cheese from Greece
72 Dining hall
73 Gardener's enemies
74 Sport group

DOWN

1 Mr.
2 Vane direction
3 Wing
4 Communicators
5 Fringe benefit
6 Advertisements
7 Expression
8 Abductor
9 Spain
10 Danish physicist
11 Blood disorder
12 Peaked
13 Caustic substance
18 European sea eagle
22 Lazy people
23 School group
24 Lawyer's title
25 Computer part
26 Technical
27 Track
29 Curve
30 Touch an animal
32 Cashew
35 Flightless bird
36 Generator
38 New York City
40 Greek god of war
41 Newly ___, Nearly Dead
42 Lingerie
43 Hustle
44 In the air (pl.)
45 Central Standard Time
46 The ___ (final word)
47 Affirmative gesture
48 Chance
51 Swell out
52 Assert
56 Medical practitioner
57 Toward the rear of the ship
59 Colors
60 Drop leave out
61 Short-term memory
62 Tell a tall tale
64 Stinger
65 Pole
66 Ball holder
67 Estimated time of arrival
68 Surface to air missile

PUZZLE 50

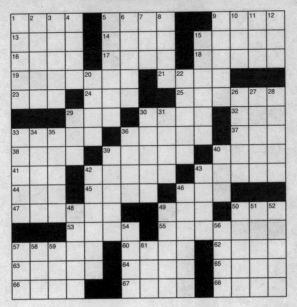

ACROSS

1 Bridge
5 Peacock blue
9 Sure
13 Naked
14 Mouser
15 City in Ohio
16 Bulb flower
17 Elapse
18 Given a ticket
19 Devotions
21 Cook in the microwave
23 Flightless bird
24 Thai
25 Angular unit
29 She
30 Reserve Officers Training Corps.
32 Cry softly
33 Lady
36 Capital of Byelorussia
37 Tax agency
38 Truant
39 Like zinc
40 Peter, for short
41 Moved quickly
42 Funeral hymn
43 Unit of electric capacitance
44 Sound
45 Brews
46 Mutt
47 Slanted font
49 Rate
50 Been
53 Colorless
55 Mistiest
57 Orange yellow
60 Egg-shaped
62 Mantle
63 Steals
64 Skim
65 Corrupt
66 Use a keyboard
67 Loop
68 Prefix ten

DOWN

1 Sharpshoot
2 Festival
3 Adios
4 Bird's home
5 Look
6 Similar
7 Ship initials
8 Association (abbr.)
9 Slid on the snow
10 Creative work
11 Contender
12 The __ (final word)
15 Antiaircraft gun (slang)
20 Detail
22 Salaam
26 Colder
27 Artery
28 Smelled
29 Movie 2001's talking computer
30 Peals
31 One time
33 __ Gras
34 Wait for
35 Title of Italian woman
36 Heavy mud
39 Zip
40 Average work performance
42 Podiums
43 Lint
46 Swiss mountain cottage
48 Huge
49 Type of shorts
50 Braid
51 Jell-o salad
52 Inscribed stone
54 New __ (city)
56 Type of tea
57 Choose
58 Wail
59 With it
61 Wheeled vehicle

PUZZLE 51

ACROSS
1 Sailors "hey"
5 U.S. Air Force
9 River dirt
13 Volcanic rock
14 Woman
15 Say
16 Maintain
17 Opposed
18 Bad
19 Early
21 Money
23 Fall mo.
24 Poem
25 Hunting guns
29 Estimated time of arrival
30 Saturate
32 Pot
33 Stadium
36 Outlaw James
37 W.C.
38 Challenge
39 Southern girl
40 As well as
41 Hoopla
42 Monte __
43 Snappy
44 Middle
45 Pen fillers
46 Explosive
47 Afternoon nap
49 Rested
50 South southeast
53 Floor covering
55 Satires
57 Reserved
60 Engage
62 Elide
63 Type of race
64 At sea
65 Slime
66 Get together
67 Stitched together
68 Joint

DOWN
1 "Remember the __"
2 "wreak __"
3 Undisguised
4 Story
5 African country
6 Burn
7 Creative work
8 Turn a pancake
9 Workers
10 That (possessive)
11 Lease
12 Chance
15 Opposite
20 Small particle
22 Efface
26 Tranquilizes
27 Jagged
28 Schnozzle
29 Vane direction
30 Offers to consumers
31 Capital of Norway
33 Belonging to Eve's husband
34 Radiuses
35 Eat away
36 Yank
39 Corny
40 Inclined
42 Make look like a city dweller
43 To
46 Plaid
48 Ermine
49 Tendon
50 Game "__ Says"
51 Kidnap
52 Sugar-free brand
54 Epochs
56 Recession
57 Build up
58 Downwind
59 Bullfight cheer
61 Vane direction

PUZZLE 52

ACROSS

1 Swine
5 Asian nation
9 Ribbon
14 Black
15 N.A. Indian
16 Repent
17 Rolled chocolate candy brand
18 AM
19 Gone With the Wind's Mr. Butler
20 Covers (2 wds.)
22 Shedding outer layer
24 Container
25 Persue
26 Use
28 Director (abbr.)
29 American Federation of Teachers (abbr.)
32 Coral reef
33 Fights
35 For
36 Dickens' "__ of Two Cities"
(2 wds.)
37 Fall mo.
38 Snappy
40 Representative
41 Biblical woman
43 Rub
44 Be nosey
45 Time zone
46 Imitative
47 Island
49 Type of Buddhism
50 Stroke (3 wds.)
53 Cousins of weasel
57 Adjust
58 Opaque gem
60 Swiss-like cheese
61 Chili con __
62 Exotic
63 Do it again
64 Massage
65 Young Women's Christian Association
66 Hitch

DOWN

1 Fennel
2 Band instrument
3 Precious metal
4 Type of winter fight
5 Resistance
6 Secure
7 Rainy mo.
8 Centennial minus ten
9 __ Gras
10 Type of alcohol
11 Bucks wives
12 Opposed
13 Allows
21 Cliff dwelling birds
23 Socialism's Marx
26 Say
27 Slippery
28 Ticket to a performance
29 Recesses
30 Crisp
31 Children
32 Retired persons association (abbr.)
33 On campus housing
34 Da Vinci's "Last __"
39 Computers' partners
42 Water (Sp.)
46 Rhododendron
47 __ Carta
48 Blemished
50 Mob
51 Dash
52 Exhaust
53 Artist Chagall
54 Adam's garden
55 Nothing
56 Haze
59 Animal foot

PUZZLE 53

ACROSS
1 Far away
5 Mexican sandwich
9 Organic compound
14 South American nation
15 On top
16 Winter wear
17 Bulb flower
18 Ring
19 Synthetic fabric
20 _____ Angels (MLB team)
22 Pronoun
24 Extension (abbr.)
25 Candy bar Baby ___
26 Radiuses
28 Short-term memory
29 Abdominal muscles (abbr.)
32 Plate armor
33 Aqualung
35 Buck's mate
36 Charred
37 Pallid
38 Emblem
40 Vane direction
41 River
43 Monarch
44 Ball holder
45 Explosive
46 Nautical "friend"
47 Wall support
49 Hoopla
50 Tail saying bird
53 Crashed
57 Add on
58 Change
60 Costa __
61 Drive away
62 Thoughtless
63 Truant
64 Cut down
65 Popular stadium
66 Prong

DOWN
1 Capital of Western Samoa
2 Spore plant
3 Opera solo
4 Barged (2 wds.)
5 Favorite vacation island
6 Particle
7 Cry softly
8 Timely
9 Heron
10 __ and burn
11 Very large book
12 Corrupt
13 Shallow area
21 Survives
23 Desensitize
26 Utilize
27 Harmonize
28 Sparse
29 Confuse
30 Bogy
31 Oracle
32 To incite
33 Con artists
34 Rub
39 Tyrant
42 Decorative needle case
46 Ms. Stewart
47 Actor Martin
48 Levied
50 Launder
51 Wager
52 Chew
53 All-knowing
54 Chinese gooseberry
55 Economics abrv.
56 Vale
59 Morse code dash

PUZZLE 54

ACROSS
1 Equal
5 River
10 South by east
13 Go at it alone
14 Norwegian
15 Orange juice finding
16 Intelligence
17 Ridiculing remark
18 Tub spread
19 Farming club (abbr.)
21 Stars "change" of position as you move
23 Distress call
26 Genetic code
28 Reverence
29 Smooth skinned fish
32 Lighted sign
33 Lubricates
34 Obscure
36 Beep
37 Started
38 Mush
42 Plebe
43 Murky
44 Despot
46 Ensued
49 Customer
51 Umpire
52 Ram's mate
53 Increase in intensity
57 Volume (abbr.)
59 Sea bird
60 Sky-blue
62 Spoken
66 Bulb flower
67 Less cooked (as in meat)
68 Acquired Immune Deficiency Syndrome (abbr.)
69 New York City
70 Turn out
71 Eats

DOWN
1 Pounds per square inch
2 Long time
3 Imp
4 House top
5 Manic
6 Not (refix)
7 Leaky faucet noise
8 U.S. Department of Agriculture
9 Oracle
10 Glum
11 Baby sheep sound
12 Type of glue
15 Childhood disease
20 Food and drug administration (abbr.)
22 Copied
23 Scotsman
24 American state
25 Grainery
27 Bowed
30 Mountain Standard Time
31 Young boys Rags-to-riches author
32 Abbess
35 Not inner
37 Saloon
38 Cubic centimeter
39 Wager
40 Alter
41 Dr. Jekyll and Mr. ___
42 Socialism's Marx
44 Recurrent
45 Enthusiasms
47 Stark
48 Alien's spaceship
49 Initiate
50 Excessive interest
54 Retired persons association (abbr.)
55 Russian ruler
56 European monetary unit
58 Linger
61 Pastor (abbr.)
63 River (Spanish)
64 Hoopla
65 Acid

PUZZLE 55

ACROSS
1 Tiff
5 Supernatural
10 Head cover
13 Meat alternative
14 Eskimo home
15 GS
16 Baseball glove
17 Debates
18 Acting (abbr.)
19 Alien's spaceship
21 Saturate with water
23 Contender
26 Ship initials
28 Donald's girlfriend
29 State of being hardened
32 Bluish white metal
33 Borrowed money
34 Machine man
36 Demonstration
37 Capital of Japan
38 Asian country
42 Plebe
43 Island
44 Stick candy bar brand
46 Abated
49 Wield
51 Her
52 Estimated time of arrival
53 Clemency
57 The other half of Jima
59 Institution (abbr.)
60 Swiss mathematician
62 Back talk
66 Bucks wives
67 More able
68 Place
69 The __ (final word)
70 Pulls in
71 Bode

DOWN
1 Short-term memory
2 Luau dish
3 American Federation of Teachers (abbr.)
4 Ballet skirt
5 White-flowered plant
6 Past
7 Radiate
8 Small particle
9 Purchase amount
10 Recurrent
11 Singing parts
12 "This little __ went to market..."
15 Plastic wrap
20 Ermine
22 Change
23 Crimp
24 Band instrument
25 Swiss-like cheese
27 Prepared young fish
30 Card game
31 Bumpkin
32 San Diego attraction
35 Computer memory units
37 Exert
38 Winter hazard
39 Ancient German character
40 To incite
41 Nothing
42 Quote
44 Tightened up
45 Written things
47 Bakes unshelled eggs
48 Tailor
49 Suppress
50 Xe
54 Approach
55 Chop
56 Women's magazine
58 Capital of Norway
61 Elver
63 Place
64 Visit
65 Star

PUZZLE 56

ACROSS

1 France & Germany river
5 Small bunch of flowers
10 Sheep
14 U.S. Department of Agriculture
15 Girl in Wonderland
16 Notion
17 Stack of paper
18 Gas
19 Sated
20 Within the sound of voice
22 Snuggled
24 Vane direction
25 Sample
26 Inflatable safety device in automobiles
30 Eight
32 Cocky
33 Blurry (2 wds.)
37 List of names
38 Maturity
39 Expires
41 Element No
44 Move bike wheels
45 Valley
46 Lucidly
47 Suggest
50 Pouch
51 Decide
53 Taught
58 Middle East dweller
59 Book by Homer
61 Ritual
62 Dawdle
63 Computer characters
64 German city
65 Celebrity
66 Desires
67 Remain

DOWN

1 Definite
2 At sea
3 Jewish calendar month
4 Professional football team
5 Skirt
6 Eating dish
7 Free of
8 Computer picture button
9 Hereditary
10 Pinches
11 Grown-up
12 Scrimmage
13 Bare scalp
21 Chief
23 Type of boat
26 Rainy mo.
27 Flatten
28 Rolled chocolate candy brand
29 Flower start
30 In style
31 Detail
33 Nab
34 Adam's garden
35 Military officer
36 Valid
40 Tricky
42 Corrupt
43 From Latvia
44 Agreement
46 Saudi Arabian citizens
47 Ross ___, philanthropist
48 City
49 Solemn
50 Stuffy
51 Knocks (2 wds.)
52 Otherwise
54 Globes
55 Revel
56 Bunsen burner
57 Renounce
60 Winter hazard

PUZZLE 57

ACROSS
1 __ fide
5 Lady
10 Vertex
14 Sonata
15 Swelling
16 Dining or living ending
17 Rice wine
18 Sounds
19 Sage
20 Meat knife
22 Small bumps
24 Cation
25 Desires
26 Cut stone
30 Bunny
32 Escargot
33 Multiple molecule compounds
37 Sock's wound
38 Expression of surprise
39 Deliberate
41 Clear beef broth
44 Light emitting __

45 Fades
46 Wickerwork stuff
47 Puny
50 Brains
51 Eucharist
53 Programs
58 Knit
59 Adult insect
61 European monetary unit
62 Hot cereal
63 African country
64 Upon
65 Region
66 Total
67 Bird's home

DOWN
1 Pear type
2 Opaque gem
3 Cook in the microwave
4 East
5 Shooting star
6 Beautify
7 Fox hole
8 Prayer ending
9 Mason's work
10 Bicker
11 Might
12 Customs
13 Flightless birds
21 Bottle
23 View as
26 Tree
27 Prig
28 Nimbus
29 Place
30 Hostess creation
31 Actor Alda
33 Heel of hand
34 Shine
35 Dig

36 Carbonated drink
40 X
42 Lazily
43 Swinging
44 Court
46 Hardships
47 Scrub clean
48 Elk-like animal
49 Omega's partner
50 Earnings
51 __ matter
52 Ruler
54 Lighted sign
55 Sand pile
56 Branch of learning
57 Chimney dirt
60 Past

PUZZLE 58

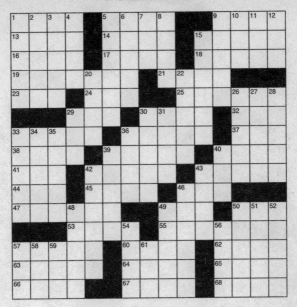

ACROSS

1 Taxis
5 Green Gables dweller
9 Gripping tool
13 Capital of Norway
14 Can not
15 Stitch
16 Russian ruler
17 Flat
18 Stadium
19 Deep-fried chip
21 Acting (abbr.)
23 Skit
24 Cubic centimeter
25 Ideal place
29 Constrictor snake
30 Painful
32 Hotel
33 For goodness __!
36 Hot liquid burn
37 Thai
38 Pennsylvania (abbr.)
39 Acrid
40 Heaps
41 Unrefined metal
42 Before Fri.
43 Recipient
44 Fat
45 Goad
46 Gal's pal
47 House cat
49 Expression of surprise
50 Task
53 Cat cries
55 Make dirty
57 Marriage site
60 Not that
62 Wager
63 Chimes
64 Father's sister
65 Stair
66 Dole out
67 Pleads
68 Sticky black substances

DOWN

1 Terra __ (type of clay)
2 Association (abbr.)
3 Bomb
4 Classify
5 Spiritual boredom
6 Having to do with the navy
7 North northeast
8 Bunsen burner
9 Virgo the Virgin
10 Winter hazard
11 Boy
12 Estimated time of arrival
15 Stroked, like a pet
20 Famous cookies
22 Permed
26 Support
27 Stupid
28 Flavoring
29 TV lawyer Matlock
30 Make a basket
31 Grow acorns
33 Parody
34 Eagle's nest
35 Bell stroke
36 Self-righteous
39 Harpy
40 Fiddle
42 Radios
43 Twofold
46 Spirits
48 Mental sight
49 Impersonating
50 Governing group
51 Finned mammal
52 Pager noises
54 Prick
56 End
57 High naval rank (abbr.)
58 Tell a tall tale
59 Explosive
61 Color

PUZZLE 59

ACROSS
1 Tell
5 Tides
9 Brand of cotton tipped stick
13 Unite
14 Ponder, with "over"
15 Business wear
16 Chimney dirt
17 Small particle
18 Cola
19 Combined effort of two
21 Item for sale
23 Poem
24 Tax agency
25 Streamer
29 Vane direction
30 Sailors
32 Southwestern Indian
33 Splinter of glass
36 Vial
37 Toupee
38 Metal thread
39 Quake
40 U.S. Department of Agriculture
41 Wrath
42 Internal structure
43 Proposal position
44 Bog
45 Unpredictable
46 River (Spanish)
47 Spell
49 Stake
50 Butane
53 Throw out
55 Locate
57 Mischievous
60 Account (abbr.)
62 Hello!
63 Oklahoma city
64 Earn
65 Women's magazine
66 Malaria
67 Post-traumatic stress disorder
68 Sleigh

DOWN
1 Operatic bass
2 Architect Frank __ Wright
3 Isolated
4 Computer memory unit
5 Emigrant
6 Water markers
7 Deli order
8 Salad
9 Female aristocrat
10 End
11 That (possessive)
12 Pounds per square inch
15 Spread out on the couch
20 Layer
22 Right angle to a ships length
26 Care for
27 Musical composition
28 Royal
29 Bard's before
30 Hunt
31 Heave
33 Sudden
34 Boss
35 Stadium
36 Money
39 Fireproof storage areas
40 Card game
42 Llama's cousin
43 Soaring plaything
46 Hired
48 Twang
49 Does' husbands
50 Broil
51 Dickens' "__ of Two Cities" (2 wds.)
52 Pushed away
54 Tap in lightly
56 Pros
57 Estimated time of arrival
58 Drag
59 Contagious disease
61 Pet

PUZZLE 60

ACROSS

1 Swill
5 Oval
10 Break
14 Stop
15 Shattered
16 Cab
17 Ca. University
18 Soil
19 Black bird
20 Is
21 Snaky fish
22 Shake
24 Sea North of the Aleutian Islands
26 Writer Bombeck
27 Food and drug administration (abbr.)
28 Run
29 Chinese seasoning
32 Tennis player Steffi
35 Orange cheese
36 Precedes an alias
37 African country
39 Olden
40 Pay
42 Poem
43 Misrepresent
45 Brand
46 Sleeping place
47 Nimbus
48 Adorn
50 Right-winger
51 Barge (2 wds.)
55 Silly
58 Tub spread
60 Wing
61 Consider
62 Show
64 Rift
65 Partial
66 Shade
67 Bushed
68 Organization of Petroleum Exporting Countries
69 Sources of inspiration
70 Whirl

DOWN

1 Young pigeon
2 Loot
3 Tanker
4 School group
5 Mexican food brand
6 Bottle
7 Car rental agency
8 X
9 Listed
10 Capital of Bangladesh
11 Nimbus
12 Brake
13 Elias ___, sewing machine
21 The ___ (final word)
23 Smudge
25 Unpredictable
26 Avoid
28 Folded sheet of paper
29 Mom
30 Scan
31 Fence opening
32 Ball
33 Travel by horse
34 Upon restful furniture
35 Geez!
38 Detest
41 Ceases
44 Hearing necessity
48 Athletic fields
49 Duet
50 Cloak
52 Compelled to go
53 Book by Homer
54 Dapper
55 As well as
56 Page
57 Identical
58 Globes
59 Decoy
63 Flightless bird
64 South by east

PUZZLE 61

ACROSS
1 Flying mammals
5 Capital of Bangladesh
10 Parts of plays
14 Flightless birds
15 Widely known
16 European monetary unit
17 Diet
18 One-celled animal
19 Speak indistinctly
20 Less than two
21 Harvested
22 Purplish color
24 Pathetic
26 Bunch of hay
27 One of these
28 Permission to enter a foreign country
29 Microgram
32 Northeast by north
35 Fate
36 Wrath
37 Alpha's opposite
39 Bullfight cheer
40 Spice
42 Mr.
43 Actress Day
45 Compass point
46 European sea eagle
47 Colored
48 Ram's mate
50 Roman garments
51 Nun
55 Come off
58 Speedy
60 Card game
61 Golf tournament
62 __ cotta (clay)
64 Singing voice
65 Mountain top
66 Character Dick
67 Carpe __
68 Snaky fish
69 Promises
70 Energetic

DOWN
1 Underneath
2 Type of acid
3 Scholar
4 South southeast
5 "You'll pay __ for this!"
6 Vertex
7 Inform
8 Auto
9 Characteristic traits from old ancestor
10 Fable writer
11 Select
12 Opp. of false
13 Classify
21 Ammo. holder
23 Abraham's son
25 Tooth
26 Lines
28 Legal
29 Mummer
30 Baby's bed
31 DNA component
32 Prow
33 Ruler
34 Capital of Switzerland
35 Divided nation
38 Special case only (2 wds.)
41 Usages
44 Should (2 wds.)
48 School writings
49 Brains
50 Military weapons
52 Spring flower
53 Make a record of
54 Spacious
55 Idiot
56 Fencing sword
57 Duck
58 Order
59 Curve
63 Time period
64 Advertisements

PUZZLE 62

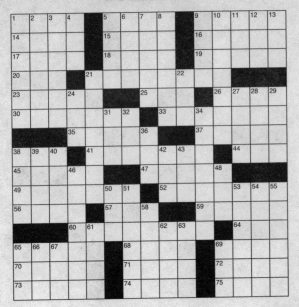

ACROSS

1 Extinct bird
5 Belt up
9 City
14 Little Mermaid's love
15 Brand of sandwich cookie
16 Wild dog
17 Can not
18 Chime
19 Sculptured heads
20 Snacked
21 Fitful
23 __ code
25 Adjust
26 Opposed
30 Proofread
33 Estimators
35 Tally (2 wds.)
37 Stairway post
38 Nuke
41 Cold medicine
44 Visit
45 Favored
47 Dike
49 Capital of Iraq
52 Amuck
56 Soviet Union
57 That man
59 City
60 Long, dramatic musical composition
64 Learn by reading
65 Supply
68 Travel around
69 Points
70 Boasts
71 Capital of Norway
72 Notion
73 Could
74 Was looked at
75 Cincinnati baseball team

DOWN

1 Depart suddenly
2 Speech maker
3 Money
4 Fall mo.
5 Clinton's VP
6 Bulb flower
7 Leases
8 Sharp angled path
9 Globes
10 Salami
11 Abdominal muscles (abbr.)
12 Baby fox
13 Advertisements
21 Declined
22 Estimated time of arrival
24 Distress call
27 Nightly tv show
28 Leaf maker
29 Island
31 Flightless bird
32 Flop
34 Experience
36 Crony
38 Asian humped ox
39 Alack's partner
40 Hogs
42 Valentine mo.
43 First woman
46 In the midst of
48 Vane direction
50 Expression of surprise
51 "me too"s
53 Write in code
54 Immobile
55 River
58 Elk-like animal
61 Repose
62 Law
63 Flatten
65 Large computer company
66 __ Lanka
67 Droop
69 Director (abbr.)

PUZZLE 63

ACROSS
1 Way
5 Two good friends
9 BB Player Abdul Jabar
14 Tub spread
15 Little Mermaid's love
16 Infra's opposite
17 Powdered drink
18 Thoughtless
19 Ground
20 Poisonous snake
21 Court summons
23 Work carelessly
25 Chinese sauce
26 Wading bird
30 Leia's pursuer (2 wds.)
33 Liberal
35 Meeting
37 Plunder
38 Air
41 Canadian city
44 Female (abr.)
45 Bit
47 Stupid
49 Given
52 Force out
56 Father
57 Hair stuff
59 Revoke
60 Toasted chewy bread roll type (2 wds.)
64 Women's partners
65 Shoe leather
68 Serving dish
69 French Sudan
70 Muslim's religion
71 Eye
72 A cozy room (2 wds.)
73 Utters
74 Looked at a book
75 Do it again

DOWN
1 Chemical salt
2 Mainland State
3 Pin
4 Shoat
5 South American nation
6 Middle East dweller
7 What a small child does
8 What children attend
9 Association (abbr.)
10 From Kuwait
11 Environmental protection agency (abbr.)
12 Make a mistake
13 Crazy
21 Romped
22 Peeper
24 Chinese seasoning
27 Hit
28 Island
29 Prow
31 W.C.
32 Possessive pronoun
34 ___ lobe, front brain section
36 Luau dish
38 Baths
39 Chinese gooseberry
40 52 weeks
42 North northeast
43 Exert
46 Of a creed
48 European sea eagle
50 Chick holder
51 Borrower
53 Like your bed
54 Fought
55 Annual storm causing current
58 Huge
61 Jewels
62 Joyful
63 Looked
65 Be seated
66 Avail
67 Wing
69 Damage

PUZZLE 64

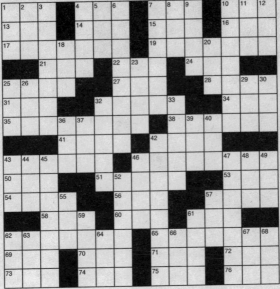

ACROSS

1 Adorn
4 Boxer Muhammad
7 Drink slowly
10 Former USSR's secret police
13 Mutt
14 Chicken
15 Digit
16 Gain
17 Caviar
19 Neighboring area
21 Wail
22 United States of America
24 Barrel
25 Colorless
27 Computer part
28 Skinny
31 Large computer company
32 Stone
34 Chance
35 Non-living wood on trees
38 3.26 light-years
41 Tush
42 Came out of sleep
43 Less colorful
46 Bullfight horsemen
50 Cashew
51 __ and burn
53 Corporate top dog
54 Type of hair do
56 Winter hazard
57 Resist
58 Fat
60 TV lawyer Matlock
61 Pain unit
62 Make stronger or larger
65 Summary
69 Morse code dash
70 Time period
71 South southeast
72 Also
73 Eye infection
74 Goof
75 Be seated
76 Distress call

DOWN

1 American Cancer Society (abbr.)
2 What's owed
3 Ancient Greek silver coin
4 Sailors "hey"
5 Sign of the zodiac
6 Initiator
7 City in Minnesota (2 wds.)
8 Note of debt
9 Fringe benefit
10 Men in shining armor
11 "To the right!"
12 Heat unit
18 Saute
20 Lease
23 Rushed
25 Relief
26 South by east
29 Wrath
30 New York City
32 Glides
33 Era
36 Dull
37 Bitty
39 Precedes an alias
40 Crimson
42 Wisdom
43 Gross national product (abbr.)
44 Regret
45 Wasting away of body
46 Walking step
47 Panthers
48 Umpire
49 Chinese sauce
52 Citizen of libya
55 Cubic centimeter
57 Period
59 Tall tales
61 Eat sparingly
62 Advertisements
63 Tangle
64 Last day of the week
66 Pounds per square inch
67 Cow speak
68 Aurora

PUZZLE 65

ACROSS

1 Advertisements
4 Make a mistake
7 Farm credit administration (abbr.)
10 Estimated time of arrival
13 Snip
14 Corporate top dog
15 Night bird
16 Facial twitch
17 Management of finances
19 Giving off soft glow
21 Relation
22 Leather worker's tool
24 Sky
25 Cusp
27 W.C.
28 African antelope
31 Note of debt
32 Movies
34 Poisonous snake
35 Envoys
38 Expenditure
41 Hit
42 Cornmeal cake
43 Eats away
46 Independence
50 Papa
51 Stocky
53 Vane direction
54 Out
56 Time period
57 Branch of learning
58 Pet
60 Molder
61 American Cancer Society (abbr.)
62 Capital of Libya
65 Incentive
69 Munch
70 Sun's name
71 Contend
72 Bard's before
73 One of these
74 Eye infection
75 The __ (final word)
76 Genetic code

DOWN

1 Brew
2 Medical practitioner
3 Piped (2 wds.)
4 Economics abbr.
5 Rock group
6 Crown (2 wds.)
7 Oblige
8 Communication Workers of America (abr.)
9 __ matter
10 Forever
11 Can metal
12 Skit
18 Nothing
20 Colossal
23 Courts
25 Relief
26 Luau dish
29 United States of America
30 Snoop
32 Break
33 Dirty
36 Acid
37 IOU part
39 Card game
40 X
42 Reputed
43 Environmental protection agency (abbr.)
44 Propel with oars
45 Sate of being opaque
46 Hairdo
47 Electromagnetism discoverer
48 Mountain Standard Time
49 Aye
52 Spookily
55 Talk
57 Whiz
59 Flip
61 Copied
62 Thirst quencher
63 Moved quickly
64 Oodles
66 Least amount
67 Pot
68 Body of water

PUZZLE 66

ACROSS
1 Juno
5 Wishes
10 Teen disease
14 Concluded
15 Spooky
16 Sailors "hey"
17 Where a necklace goes
18 Manhattan's neighbor
19 Split
20 Genetic code
21 Black
22 Crustacean
24 Early pain relieving drug
26 Sports channel
27 __ Francisco
28 Fancy car
29 Ewe's mate
32 Holler
35 Happy
37 Unite
39 Lotion ingredients
41 Avail
42 Huge
43 Elite intellectuals' society
44 Cootie
46 Jewish scribe
47 Drunkard
48 Exploiter
50 College football conference (abbr.)
52 Pock
53 Mourner
57 Desires
60 Star Trek Automoton's
61 Unrefined metal
62 Den
63 Island nation
65 Italian currency
66 Reside
67 Enable
68 Won
69 Dash
70 Terraced walkway
71 Stacked mattresses

DOWN
1 Makers of the Accord
2 Smoothes
3 Summary
4 Raiders of the Lost __ (Harrison Ford movie)
5 Spider trap ingredient
6 Wading bird
7 Flatten
8 Least amount
9 Discrimination
10 Moses' brother
11 Nick
12 De __ (from the beginning)
13 Looked
21 Time period
23 Water faucet
25 Islands
26 Bedspread feather
28 Intense light beam
29 Round cracker brand
30 Far away
31 Asian starling
32 Sweet potatoes
33 Tub spread
34 Accustomed
36 Type of gun
38 Sibling's daughter
40 Food covering
45 Unites
49 Fabric belts
51 Fruit
52 Wailing warning
53 Risen (2 wds.)
54 Utter
55 Goofed
56 Learns
57 Women's magazine
58 Nab
59 Brand of milk
60 Stay
64 Picnic pest
65 Scientist's office

PUZZLE 67

ACROSS
1 Truth
5 Demobilize
10 Knocks (2 wds.)
14 Pound
15 Type of acid
16 Brand of sandwich cookie
17 Wrack
18 Walker
19 Retired persons association (abbr.)
20 Snacked
21 Carry
22 Verse meter
24 Distorts
26 Ceases
27 Popeye's yes
28 Wise
29 Resort hotel
32 Saucer
35 Not mine
37 Roman Catholic Church heads
39 Make a record of
41 Hotel
42 Cut of beef
43 Repent
44 Desire
46 Bunsen burner
47 __ Jones Industrial average
48 Ooze
50 __ you! (attention getter)
52 Suffer
53 Forded
57 Groups of ships
60 Anon
61 Caesar's three
62 Holes
63 Midwestern state denizen
65 Do it again
66 Canal
67 Efface
68 Elderly
69 Thoughtfulness
70 Leases
71 "as you __"

DOWN
1 Unit of electric capacitance
2 Keen
3 Leader
4 X
5 Former name for Benin
6 Gives off
7 Microphone
8 Less than two
9 Tiresome
10 Wanders
11 Middle East dweller
12 South American nation
13 Drenches
21 Chance
23 Dextrous
25 Made of oak
26 Merits
28 Day's beginning
29 Descry
30 Pennsylvania (abbr.)
31 At sea
32 Kaput
33 Within
34 Store
36 Tanker
38 Complies
40 Set to zero
45 King's seats
49 Not as difficult
51 Long time
52 Surround
53 Move effortlessly
54 Attack
55 Bedspread feather
56 Light emitting __
57 Gall
58 Italian currency
59 Great
60 Cob
64 Unrefined metal
65 Half-baked

PUZZLE 68

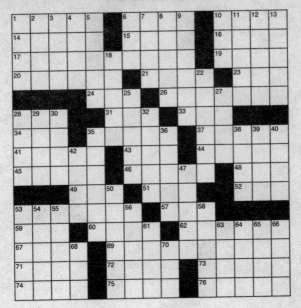

ACROSS

1 Strong drink
6 Journalist's question
10 Won
14 Tight at the top, flaring at the bottom (2 wds.)
15 Stay
16 Japanese dress
17 Reminder note
19 Joint
20 Wax __
21 Spy
23 Fall mo.
24 Extremely high frequency (abbr.)
26 Johns
28 Constrictor snake
31 Bolus
33 Body of water
34 Kimono sash
35 Makes a sound like a lion
37 Limber
41 Approximate date
43 Snooze
44 What babies do
45 Made lock openers
46 Curtails
48 Aye
49 Pluto
51 Goose egg
52 South southeast
53 Small keyboard instrument
57 Chewy stuff
59 Color
60 Juno
62 Cooks
67 __ matter
69 High ranking clergy
71 Rivalry
72 Double agent
73 Dard
74 Goofs
75 Moved through the water
76 Kinds

DOWN

1 Invent
2 Tub spread
3 Ten cents
4 Tie
5 Eagle's nest
6 Compass point
7 Lurk
8 Scorched
9 Rates
10 Beg
11 Long boat
12 Construct
13 Special menus
18 Sound of a sneeze
22 Relents
25 French money
27 Den
28 Dark beer
29 Off-Broadway award
30 Incorporeal
32 Strength
35 Sharp tasting vegetable
36 Small bunch of flowers
38 Children's love
39 Garden tools
40 Otherwise
42 Give
47 Ad
50 Vapors
53 Irritate
54 Swiss mathematician
55 Monkey's cousin
56 Indian weapon
58 Wet
61 Organization concerned with civil liberties (abbr.)
63 Colorless
64 Big boat
65 Firm up muscles
66 Baths
68 Advertisements
70 Skirt edge

PUZZLE 69

ACROSS
1 Presents
6 Central points
10 Acting (abbr.)
14 Dope
15 Dreary
16 Catch
17 Renewable
19 Triad
20 City in Pakistan
21 Father
23 Bolus
24 Mr..'s wife
26 Not completely broken
28 Bashful
31 Highs
33 American Cancer Society (abbr.)
34 Sign of the zodiac
35 Dimensions
37 Direct
41 Musical instrument
43 New York City
44 Ridiculing remark
45 Give essential information
46 Thrill
48 Charge
49 Track
51 Bard's before
52 Writing liquid
53 1800's Italian secret society
57 Madagascar franc (abbr.)
59 Bullfight cheer
60 National capital
62 Two-dimensional
67 Slant
69 Foolishness
71 Can
72 At sea
73 Afloat (2 wds.)
74 Index
75 Ribald
76 Huge

DOWN
1 Woman
2 Notion
3 Angle
4 Dorothy's dog
5 Snow heavily
6 Food and drug administration (abbr.)
7 Globes
8 Islam's head
9 European peninsula Spain's peninsula
10 Inclined
11 Fake chocolate
12 Kink
13 World map
18 Show
22 Justify
25 Chine
27 Association (abbr.)
28 Sloven
29 Frau's husband
30 Yoga practicer
32 Mode
35 Unroll
36 Tippet
38 Hi-fi
39 Adam's garden
40 Stink
42 Air (prefix)
47 Bpm
50 Clannish
53 Programming language
54 Where you were at crime time
55 What you get in restaurants
56 Entertain
58 Boast
61 Not many (2 wds.)
63 Opposed
64 Bird's home
65 Region
66 Baseball's Nolan
68 Adjust
70 Craze

PUZZLE 70

ACROSS

1 Dance
6 Abstains from food
11 Move away
14 Love
15 Cubic decimetre
16 W.C.
17 Race car
18 White
19 Genetic code
20 Their
22 Hand warmers
24 Central Standard Time
25 Cause of sickness
26 Legal document
27 Sap
30 Earn
32 Comforts
33 For
34 Carbonated drink
35 Hotel
36 Inflamed area
38 Hostel
42 Lease

43 Spacecraft detachments
44 Central Intelligence Agency
45 Louse
48 Yoga practicer
49 Hawk
50 Bone
51 Flying rodent
52 Football assoc.
54 Cattle house (2 wds.)
56 Involving exercise
60 Highs
61 Counterfeiter
63 Eskimo home
64 Visit
65 Natural occurrence
66 Fry lightly
67 Make a mistake
68 Overgrown
69 Massage

DOWN

1 Distort
2 Jewish calendar month
3 South of the border crazy
4 Moat
5 Nothings
6 Open tart-like pastry
7 Sky
8 Obstruct
9 Lane
10 Delivered by post
11 Seniors
12 A Scottish lass
13 Brags
21 Uttermost
23 Noise
25 Precedes an alias
27 Accountant
28 Bolus
29 Distress call
31 Advertisements
32 Ceases
34 Germ

35 Salt addition
37 Hike a mountain
38 Record
39 Winter hazard
40 Goose egg
41 Young lady
43 Cooking vessel
45 Impeach
46 Decent
47 Large rope
48 Mr. Doodle
49 Catchword
51 Heroic
53 Frolic
55 Not many (2 wds.)
56 Pretentious
57 Color
58 Small particle
59 Dorm dweller
62 The __ (final word)

PUZZLE 71

ACROSS

1 Adjust
6 Bundled hay
11 Chinese seasoning
14 Permed
15 Black
16 Note of debt
17 Lane
18 Eat away
19 Buck's mate
20 Launch (2 wds.)
22 Soul Residents
24 Vane direction
25 Crow's call
26 Eat sparingly
27 One who gets things done
30 Peewee
32 Sticky weeds
33 Ram's mate
34 Taverns
35 What a nurse gives
36 Foghorn ___
38 Release of life

42 Boxer Muhammad
43 Spore plant
44 Flightless bird
45 Give birth to a cow
48 Old Testament book
49 Mantle
50 Brand of sandwich cookie
51 Mr.
52 Elver
54 Weedy fern
56 Moderate tempo (music)
60 Chinese cooking pan
61 Time of day
63 Electronic mail
64 Peeper
65 Cove
66 Hotel
67 Shape
68 Little
69 Got up

DOWN

1 Parts of plays
2 Decoy
3 Asian country
4 Small aircraft
5 Synthetic fiber
6 Veal
7 Abridged (abbr.)
8 Peer (2 wds.)
9 Render capable
10 Tinter
11 He vanished into ___
12 Earlier
13 Visitors
21 Sports car brand
23 Elicit
25 Nervous system
27 New Jersey's neighbor
28 IOU part
29 Electroen-cephalograph (abbr.)
31 Pot
32 Blintz

34 Tree trunk
35 Soup serving bowl
37 "wreak ___"
38 Proof ending
39 Thirst quencher
40 Sports official
41 Take to court
43 Ermine
45 What a spider leaves
46 Gully
47 Revealed
48 Jangle
49 Uproar
51 River
53 Swelling
55 Loop
56 Lawyer (abbr.)
57 Treaty organization
58 Binds
59 Women's magazine
62 Chicken

PUZZLE 72

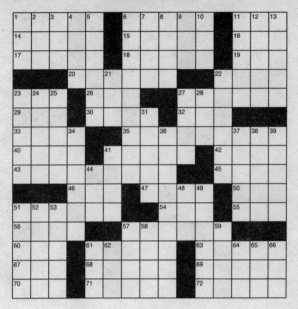

ACROSS

1 Dining need
6 Elude
11 Foreign Agricultural Service
14 Got up
15 Tournaments
16 Build up
17 Cola
18 Jumped
19 Seafood
20 Waited
22 Space ship builders
23 Highest trump in some loo
26 Extension (abbr.)
27 Steer being fattened
29 Wing
30 Tone__-
32 Poisonous snake
33 Dines
35 Swear
40 Prayer ending
41 Aleutian
42 Corrupt
43 Nasal hemorrhage
45 Staff
46 Raiders of the Lost __ (Harrison Ford movie)
47 Abundant
50 Buck's mate
51 Margarine brand
54 Cooky
55 Make a mistake
56 Feverish
57 Fruit acid
60 Eye infection
61 Waitress on Cheers
63 Cooks
67 Male cat
68 Sell
69 Slack
70 Bard's before
71 Become tight
72 Musical composition

DOWN

1 Teaspoon (abbr.)
2 Snacked
3 Hit
4 Deprivation
5 Rewrote
6 Altar (2 wds.)
7 Fencing sword
8 Kaput
9 Gross national product (abbr.)
10 Time zone
11 Unit of electric capacitance
12 Got up
13 Smudge
21 Hatchet
22 He made you an uncle
23 Encomium
24 "Remember the __"
25 Spouses
27 Speedy
28 Sixth sense
31 Ridicule
34 Underhanded
36 Cassette
37 Circumvent
38 Opp. of major
39 Old
41 Alcoholic
44 Lingerie
48 Popular president's initials
49 Nonpoisonous
51 Glue
52 Performer
53 Clue and shoe, for example
57 Ocean Spray's drink starters
58 Evils
59 Bird
61 Central Standard Time
62 Whiz
64 Note of debt
65 Acid
66 Visit

PUZZLE 73

ACROSS

1 Host
6 Strength
11 Skit
14 Glides
15 Noose
16 Thai
17 Infant's crying disease
18 Remaining one
19 Peaked
20 Fastidious
22 Women's magazine
23 Wail
26 The __ (final word)
27 Grammar
29 W.C.
30 Repose
32 Wooden leg
33 Chances of winning
35 Clergy ruling body
40 Long-suffering
41 Tire

42 Region
43 Polygon surrounded solid
45 Tail-less cat
46 Downwind
47 Eve's husband
50 __ Lanka
51 Punk hairdo
54 __ league school
55 Possessive pronoun
56 Middle East dweller
57 Get at
60 Bad (prefix)
61 Country house
63 Squabbles
67 Deli order
68 Aleutian
69 Eskimo home
70 Abdominal muscles (abbr.)
71 Very tiny fly
72 Butter maker

DOWN

1 Escudo
2 Cow speak
3 Calorie
4 Little Mermaid's love
5 Artist of illusion
6 Killing
7 Rodents
8 Colorless
9 Avail
10 Neither's partner
11 Tipped
12 Lily-like plant
13 Brand of floor cleaner
21 Less than two
22 Memory trace
23 Walk noisily
24 Cowboy show
25 Warble
27 Energetic
28 Yes
31 Jeweled headdress
34 Space platform

36 Destroy
37 Clang
38 __ Matisse, painter
39 Up or down on a graph
41 Time period
44 Carve
48 Street abbr.
49 Snapple's competitor
51 Small wrapped candies
52 Toothbrush brand
53 Stops moving
57 Won
58 Drink quickly
59 Sound of relief
61 Reservoir
62 Boxer Muhammad
64 Contagious disease
65 Pro
66 Boy

PUZZLE 74

ACROSS

1 Serving of corn
4 Use money
9 School group
12 Alliance
14 Written material
15 Record
16 Elizabeth's nickname
17 Field
18 East
19 Strike workers
21 Eskimo home
23 French "yes"
24 Sleep disorder
26 Disaster
29 Childhood nightmare character (2 wds.)
33 Sports official
34 Gift
36 Street abbr.
37 Damage
38 South southeast
39 Bard's before
42 Second to last month

43 Pride
44 More confident
46 Stretch to make do
47 Contribution given
51 Volcanic depression
53 Bpm
54 Long time
55 Muslim's religion
57 Pressers
60 Austin novel
61 Sap (2 wds.)
65 Dimwit
67 Sonata
68 Cook with dry heat
69 Fencing sword
70 Fast plane
71 Painter Richard
72 Ram's mate

DOWN

1 Move away
2 Brews
3 Reserve Officers Training Corps.
4 Judicial business meetings
5 Pacific Standard Time
6 Vane direction
7 Snooze
8 Coloring
9 El __
10 Triad
11 Precedes an alias
13 Turmoil
15 Thailand's Peninsula
20 Does' husbands
22 "To the right!"
24 Most basic
25 Fire irons
26 Boiled
27 Adult insect
28 Cook's garb
30 Impressionist painter

31 Arouse
32 At no time
35 Fable writer
40 Chits
41 Inaccuracy
45 Card game
48 Book of facts
49 Thirst quencher
50 Put away
52 Positive electrode
55 Pixies
56 Indecent language
58 Uh-uh
59 Killed
60 Aurora
62 Distress call
63 Munch
64 Avail
66 Ball holder

PUZZLE 75

ACROSS

1 Unpleasant
4 Paired sock
9 Morse code dash
12 Mined metals
14 Sporty car brand
15 Opp. of early
16 Page
17 Pointed weapon
18 Aroma
19 Ran out
21 Utter
23 Corporate top dog
24 Abhorrence
26 Rise
29 Airfoil length
33 Constrictor snake
34 Emblem
36 Expression of surprise
37 American Federation of Teachers (abbr.)
38 Less than two
39 Estimated time of arrival
42 Representative
43 Be seated
44 Whining voice type
46 Exhaust
47 Spring-time allergies (2 wds.)
51 An amusing play
53 Gone With the Wind's Mr. Butler
54 Scriptural your
55 Irritate
57 Fasten
60 Shinny
61 Synthetic fabric
65 Frost
67 Valentines Day color
68 Ills
69 Energetic
70 Picnic pest
71 Dales
72 Stretch to make do

DOWN

1 Curtsy
2 Greek god of war
3 Insightful
4 Mammoth cousin
5 American College of Physicians (abbr.)
6 Second day of the week
7 Time period
8 "Origin of the Species" author
9 Pedestal part
10 On top
11 She
13 Mace
15 Towers over
20 Slow
22 Arms clasped
24 IOU part
25 Coins
26 Embarrass
27 National capital
28 Mean
30 Analyze syntactically
31 In the lead
32 Frizzy
35 Lore
40 Inept
41 Hawaiian 'hello'
45 Creative work
48 Nickname for Frankenstein
49 Extremely high frequency (abbr.)
50 Skewed
52 Legends
55 Jaw
56 Insinuate
58 Manage
59 Listen
60 Resort hotel
62 Street abbr.
63 Cubic centimeter
64 Peaked
66 Seed bread

PUZZLE 76

ACROSS

1. Time zone
4. Place
7. Possessive pronoun
10. Drench
13. Ghost's greeting
14. Got up
16. Christmas __
17. Card game
18. Looked at fondly
19. Harry
21. What babies need a lot of
23. Genetic code
24. Central Standard Time
25. Coral reef
28. Intakes
32. Papa
35. Right angle to a ships length
37. Court
38. Luck o' the __
40. Burn
41. Make a mistake
42. Ancient Indian
43. Light cake
45. Estimated time of arrival
46. Tiny amounts
47. Tax agency
48. Fiendish
51. Unrefined metal
52. Slippery frigid
53. Rock group
55. Loves
58. Right
61. Greek philosopher
62. __ you! (attention getter)
64. Negatively charged particle
66. Stubble
67. United States of America
68. Prod
69. Kid
70. X
71. Cereal

DOWN

1. Escudo
2. Played in the water
3. Tropical edible root
4. Connect
5. Cation
6. Temper
7. Slime
8. Exploiter
9. Crimson
11. Mold
12. Legislative assembly
14. Tennis player Andre
15. Engrossed
20. Exhaust
22. Winter hazard
25. Desert plants
26. Detest
27. Many months
29. Baby bird sound
30. Artery
31. Muslim sacred text
32. Horse
33. Sesame Street's grouch
34. Stage
36. Creative work
39. River (Spanish)
44. Safe keeping
46. Ice deliverer
49. Popeye's yes
50. Wrath
52. Small particle
54. List of meals
55. Singing voice
56. Scoot
57. Close
58. Baseball's Nolan
59. Antic
60. Meditation
61. Pacific Standard Time
63. Vane direction
65. Gain

PUZZLE 77

ACROSS

1 Compass point
4 Poisonous snake
7 No
10 Sell
13 Volume (abbr.)
14 Fried bread
16 Present time
17 Vane direction
18 Typing mistakes
19 Fear
21 Stood up
23 Sound
24 Picnic pest
25 Part of a min.
28 Grouping
32 Band instrument
35 Astound
37 Bog
38 Talky
40 Not yours
41 Peaked
42 Socialism's Marx
43 Flaxen
45 Seafood
46 Spooky
47 Popeye's yes
48 Go back in
51 Tree
52 Lease
53 Raiders of the Lost __ (Harrison Ford movie)
55 Thingumajig
58 Smooth
61 Looking at
62 Klutz
64 Variety show
66 Scrimmage
67 Imp
68 River
69 Ship initials
70 State
71 Limb

DOWN

1 Fast plane
2 Scotsman
3 Walk through water
4 Maintain
5 Boy
6 Guilty or not
7 Uh-uh
8 After awhile
9 Aye
11 Shortening
12 Fool's gold
14 Tight wad, for example
15 Saclike structures filled with fluid or diseased matter
20 Less than two
22 Moved quickly
25 Dance
26 Author Dickinson
27 Long boat
29 Ablaze
30 Casaba
31 Cove
32 Extra
33 Month
34 Woody part of plants
36 Type of Buddhism
39 Whiz
44 Pick up
46 Inaccuracies
49 Estimated time of arrival
50 Serving of corn
52 Sole
54 Joint
55 Colors
56 Lubricates
57 Bucks wives
58 Unpredictable
59 Corrupt
60 Sand pile
61 Flightless bird
63 Wing
65 Electroen-cephalograph (abbr.)

PUZZLE 78

ACROSS

1 McDonald's "Big __"
4 Boxer Muhammad
7 Wrestling mat
10 Tree
13 Wooden sheet
14 However
15 Kimono sash
16 Avail
17 Programmer
19 Saddle horse
21 Diet
22 Run
23 Gofer
25 Distrust
29 Garret
32 Pig pens
34 Pride
35 Book of facts
36 Little bit
37 Maybe
40 Sixth sense
41 Tax agency
42 Exhaust
43 Accountant
46 Qualify to something
48 Football assoc.
51 Records
53 Ram's mate
54 Colored People's association
56 Technical
57 Smells
59 Ocean Spray's drink starters
60 Dines
62 Frau's husband
64 Ancient time piece
67 Citrus fruit drink
70 Fast plane
71 Stretch to make do
72 Build up
73 Convert into leather
74 Been
75 Rodent
76 Pod vegetable
77 Peeper

DOWN

1 Miles per hour
2 Wing
3 Geometric curve
4 To incite
5 Coaxed
6 That (possessive)
7 Papa
8 Toward the rear of the ship
9 Pickle herb
10 Halo
11 South southeast
12 __ you! (attention getter)
18 Bovine
20 Soft cloth
23 Pacific Standard Time
24 Estimated time of arrival
26 Electromagnetism discoverer
27 Expression
28 Bragger
30 Foreign Agricultural Service
31 Teaspoon (abbr.)
33 Double agents
35 Birch-like tree
38 European sea eagle
39 Crony
43 Central daylight time
44 Pastry
45 Rises
47 Other half of Jima
48 Tell
49 Farm credit admin. (abbr.)
50 Licensed practical nurse
52 African country
55 Land unit
57 City
58 British county
61 Plane
63 Austin novel
64 Compass point
65 United States of America
66 Lease
67 Lick
68 Time period
69 Vane direction

PUZZLE 79

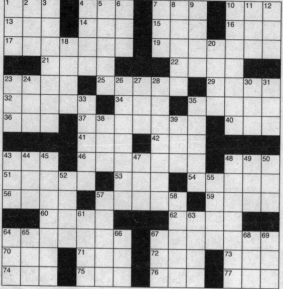

ACROSS
1 Type of partnership
4 Expression of surprise
7 Sign language
10 Wipe
13 Pastry
14 McDonald's "Big __"
15 Other half of Jima
16 American Federation of Teachers (abbr.)
17 Brother's sons
19 Reddish-purple color
21 Rate
22 Science channel
23 Cowboy fight
25 Duck
29 Omelette need
32 Afloat (2 wds.)
34 Less than two
35 Bread leftover
36 Aye
37 Computer copier
40 Snacked
41 Sedan
42 Buck's mate
43 Mass transport
46 Strangeness
48 Implore
51 Found
53 Serving of corn
54 Simultaneous gunshots
56 Roman garments
57 Meeting
59 Expired
60 Soviet Union
62 Epochs
64 _____ Angels (MLB team)
67 Winker
70 Average work performance
71 Sign of the zodiac
72 Alternative (abbr.)
73 Sixth sense
74 Pride
75 Acid
76 South southeast
77 Rock group

DOWN
1 Licensed practical nurse
2 Truss
3 Deject
4 Prayer ending
5 Peddles
6 American Cancer Society (abbr.)
7 Place
8 Elegant
9 Company symbol
10 Nicaragua capital
11 Often poetically
12 School group
18 Compel to go
20 Always
23 Time period
24 Southwestern Indian
26 Money pincher
27 Hotel
28 Provides
30 Time zone
31 South by east
33 Large wide scarf
35 Leafy salad green
38 Bounder
39 Aurora
43 Stake
44 Card game
45 ___ Cactus Blossom, AZ state flower
47 No
48 Foot nuisance
49 First woman
50 Deity
52 Money
55 Jewish calendar month
57 Tests
58 Utters
61 Hawk
63 Ritual
64 Monkey
65 Badger
66 Modern
67 Foreign Agricultural Service
68 Vane direction
69 Revolutions per minute

PUZZLE 80

ACROSS

1 Advertisements
4 Vapor
9 Pride
12 Knocks (2 wds.)
14 Arrival
15 Inform
16 Applaud
17 Nomad
18 Actor Alda
19 Muslim's religion
21 Stomach sore
23 Car rental agency
25 Descry
26 Capital of Japan
29 Pet
31 Lubricated
35 Environmental protection agency (abbr.)
36 Hottest
39 French "yes"
40 Make a mistake
41 Rounded part
42 Wing
43 Mayan

44 Bright (2 wds.)
46 X
47 Sculpt
49 Downwind
50 Orange yellow
52 Christmas meats
54 Thoughtless
56 City
58 Victimizing
61 African antelope
62 Access (2 wds.)
66 Prong
68 Land unit
69 Adult insect
70 Kill
71 "To the right!"
72 Dice
73 Ram's mate

DOWN

1 Curve
2 Painter of melting clocks
3 Baths
4 Italian physicist
5 Card game
6 I want my ___
7 Bard's before
8 Pancake need
9 Women's magazine
10 Hiking equipment
11 Possess
13 Spread out
15 Desert plants
20 Assure
22 Swag
24 Coiled papers
25 Robber
26 Swarms
27 Ms. Winfrey
28 Fate
30 Walk slowly
32 Unwilling
33 Swiss

mathematician
34 Waitress on "Cheers"
37 Brew
38 ___ Lanka
44 Flimsy
45 Flip
48 Stage
51 Children
53 Supernatural
55 Cars
56 One time
57 Definite
59 Egyptian river
60 Chew
61 Quip
63 Flightless bird
64 Charge
65 Maturity
67 Peeper

PUZZLE 81

ACROSS

1. Beats per minute
4. Utter
9. Typing rate
12. Spoken
14. Dope
15. Satiate
16. Yoga practicer
17. Whinny
18. Asian country
19. Forceful but brief
21. Ups or downs on a graph
23. Assist
25. Rift
26. Wigwam
29. High naval rank (abbr.)
31. Rhinoceros
35. First woman
36. Skin disease
39. Distress call
40. Headed
41. Bourn
42. Most basic
43. Time period
44. Nonliving
46. Wing
47. Woody part of plants
49. Rate
50. Stomach sore
52. __ vu
54. GS
56. Type of acid
58. Facial soap brand
61. Alliance
62. Purr
66. Color
68. Swag
69. Navigation system
70. Sodium
71. X
72. Gives the impression of being
73. Body of water

DOWN

1. Sonny
2. Old style plane
3. Wise Man
4. Plastic
5. Poem
6. Caesar's three
7. Tooth
8. Type of alcohol
9. Item for sale
10. Parent teacher groups
11. Women's partners
13. Limber
15. Extra sense
20. Bottom
22. Incorporeal
24. Dried & powdered red pepper
25. Evens
26. Type of communication
27. All
28. Move bike wheels
30. Slouch
32. Abraham's son
33. Upper-class
34. Sesame Street's
37. Move away
38. Slide on snow
44. Prayer ending
45. Select
48. Decree
51. Tree branches
53. Cheeks
55. Stories
56. Healing plant
57. Planet orbiter
59. Alack's partner
60. Christmas
61. Deli order
63. Garden tool
64. Wrath
65. Ewe's mate
67. Estimated time of arrival

ANSWER KEY

PUZZLE 1

PUZZLE 4

PUZZLE 2

PUZZLE 5

PUZZLE 3

PUZZLE 6

ANSWER KEY

PUZZLE 7

PUZZLE 10

PUZZLE 8

PUZZLE 11

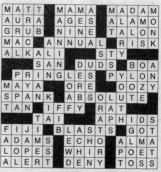

PUZZLE 9

PUZZLE 12

ANSWER KEY

PUZZLE 13

PUZZLE 16

PUZZLE 14

PUZZLE 17

PUZZLE 15

PUZZLE 18

ANSWER KEY

PUZZLE 19

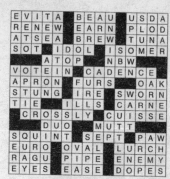

PUZZLE 22

PUZZLE 20

PUZZLE 23

PUZZLE 21

PUZZLE 24

ANSWER KEY

PUZZLE 25

PUZZLE 28

PUZZLE 26

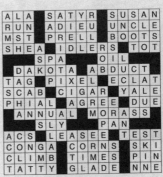

PUZZLE 29

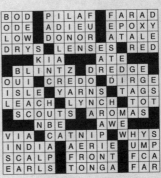

PUZZLE 27

PUZZLE 30

ANSWER KEY

PUZZLE 31

PUZZLE 34

PUZZLE 32

PUZZLE 35

PUZZLE 33

PUZZLE 36

ANSWER KEY

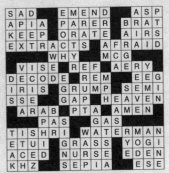

PUZZLE 37

PUZZLE 40

PUZZLE 38

PUZZLE 41

PUZZLE 39

PUZZLE 42

ANSWER KEY

PUZZLE 43

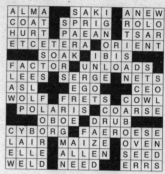

PUZZLE 46

PUZZLE 44

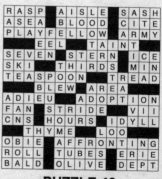

PUZZLE 47

PUZZLE 45

PUZZLE 48

ANSWER KEY

PUZZLE 49

PUZZLE 52

PUZZLE 50

PUZZLE 53

PUZZLE 51

PUZZLE 54

ANSWER KEY

PUZZLE 55

PUZZLE 58

PUZZLE 56

PUZZLE 59

PUZZLE 57

PUZZLE 60

ANSWER KEY

PUZZLE 61

PUZZLE 64

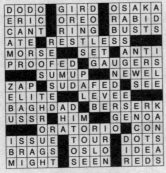

PUZZLE 62

PUZZLE 65

PUZZLE 63

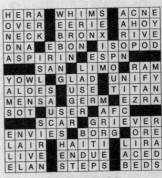

PUZZLE 66

ANSWER KEY

PUZZLE 67

PUZZLE 70

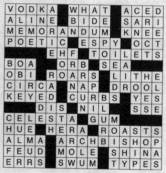

PUZZLE 68

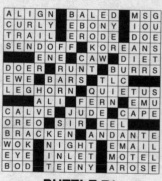

PUZZLE 71

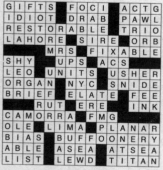

PUZZLE 69

PUZZLE 72